LIVING WITH RADIATION

National Radiological Protection Board

Preface

Living with Radiation may seem an ironic title for a book about protection against radiation, but we have to live with many types of harmful radiations either because they cannot be avoided or because they have become essential to our way of life. In any case, the title has been hallowed by usage: this is the fifth edition of the book. I am grateful to the members of staff who put it together.

Our task at NRPB is to protect people from the hazards of ionising and non-ionising radiations. We achieve this in a number of ways, by conducting research, providing support and services, and giving advice to those who make policy in government and elsewhere.

Another side of our work is to provide information on radiation. This book is part of the strategy. My hope is that it may be of interest to many readers – to teachers, journalists, environmentalists, lawyers, doctors, industrialists, officials, and politicians. My wish is that it will improve knowledge of radiation.

Roger Clarke
DIRECTOR

Contents

1 Introduction

Types of radiation

Radiation is a fact of life. Light and heat from the sun are natural forms of radiation essential to our existence. There are also other forms, which we generate in everyday life, such as microwaves for cooking, radiowaves for communication, radar for navigation, and *X-rays* for medical examinations. *Radioactive* materials also emit radiation. These materials occur naturally throughout the environment, but we have also produced others artificially.

We can classify radiation according to the effects it produces on matter. There are two categories, ionising and non-ionising radiations. *Ionising radiation* includes *cosmic rays*, X-rays, and the radiation from radioactive materials. *Non-ionising radiation* includes ultraviolet light, radiant heat, radiowaves, and microwaves.

We can also classify radiation in terms of its origin as natural radiation or artificial radiation.

Benefits and risks

The benefits from natural non-ionising radiation, mainly heat and light from the sun, are enormous, but there are no clear benefits from exposure to natural ionising radiation.

We make considerable use of both ionising and non-ionising radiations however. Artificial radiations have led to dramatic advances in medical diagnosis and treatment and are used for a wide range of procedures in industry, agriculture, and research. Nevertheless, they can be harmful to human beings, and people must be protected from unnecessary or excessive exposures.

The greatest concern about ionising radiation stems from the way in which it can cause malignant diseases in people exposed to it and inherited defects in later generations.

Some uses of radiation
IONISING RADIATION
Medical diagnosis and treatment
Nuclear power
Industrial radiography
Sterilisation of medical equipment
NON-IONISING RADIATION
Optical sources
Lighting
Heating
Measurement
Sterilisation
Electromagnetic fields
TV and radio broadcasting
Personal telecommunications

The terms in italics are explained in later chapters as well as in the glossary.

The likelihood of such effects depends on the amount of radiation that a person receives: this is equally true whether the radiation is natural or artificial. So in circumstances that we can control, we need to make a careful balance between the risks and the benefits of the procedures that expose people to radiation.

The effects of non-ionising radiation depend on the type and intensity of the radiation. Non-ionising radiation can damage the skin and the eyes; if it penetrates body tissues, it can damage internal organs by heating them. In the long term, exposure to ultraviolet radiation may cause skin cancer and cataracts. Again we need measures to protect people from such effects.

1

Introduction

....

Public anxiety

Public anxiety

As the effects of ionising and non-ionising radiations have become better understood during recent decades, a system of *radiological protection* has been developed to protect people from sources of radiation. The subject of radiation safety receives much attention in our society partly because radiation is one cause, among many, of cancer. Moreover, our senses cannot detect most forms of radiation; this undoubtedly adds to our anxiety.

Ionising radiation and laser warning symbols

Another reason for general concern may be the lack of reliable and accessible information about radiation. The aim of this book is to help by providing information for those who are not experts. In the following chapters, we describe the sources and effects of radiation of all types and explain the principles and practices of radiological protection.

2 Concepts and quantities

Structure of matter

Studies in physics and chemistry during the last two centuries have revealed that all matter consists of *atoms*. These are the basic building blocks of the *elements* such as hydrogen, carbon, oxygen, iron, and lead. Each atom contains a tiny central positively charged *nucleus* and a number of *electrons*. The electrons carry negative electric charge and move around the nucleus in clouds – or shells as they are called – with loosely defined boundaries. The nucleus is typically 10 000 times smaller than the electron clouds and the electrons themselves are too small in size to measure. This means that the atom is mainly empty and difficult to depict except in diagrams which are largely schematic.

The nucleus of the atom contains *protons,* which carry a positive charge equal to the electrons' negative charge, and *neutrons,* which carry no charge at all. (We do not need to concern ourselves here with the more fundamental structure of protons and neutrons.) Each atom contains equal numbers of protons and electrons and is therefore electrically neutral. Atoms of the same or different elements can, however, combine to form larger, uncharged entities called *molecules.* For example, 2 atoms of oxygen form 1 molecule of oxygen, and 2 atoms of hydrogen combine with 1 atom of oxygen to form 1 molecule of water.

The number of protons in the nucleus, called the *atomic number,* gives an element its unique characteristics: the atomic number of carbon is 6, for instance, whereas for lead it is 82. Most of an atom's mass is concentrated in the nucleus, and the total number of protons plus neutrons is called the *mass number.*

Since the number of electrons equals the number of protons, we can specify an atomic species by the number of protons and neutrons it contains. Moreover, since the number of protons is unique to each element, we can simply use the name of the

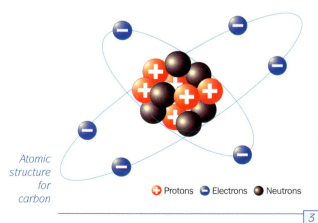

Atomic structure for carbon

⊕ Protons ⊖ Electrons ● Neutrons

element together with the mass number to specify each species or *nuclide*. So carbon-12 is a nuclide with 6 protons plus 6 neutrons. Lead-208, for comparison, is a nuclide with 82 protons and 126 neutrons.

Nuclides of an element that have the same number of protons but different numbers of neutrons are called *isotopes* of that element. Hydrogen, for instance, has three isotopes: hydrogen-1 (common hydrogen with a nucleus of only 1 proton), hydrogen-2 called deuterium (1 proton and 1 neutron), and hydrogen-3 called tritium (1 proton and 2 neutrons). Iron has 10 isotopes from iron-52 to iron-61, all with the 26 protons that characterise the element.

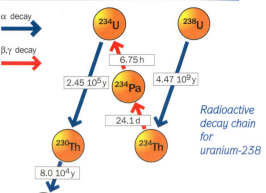

Radioactive decay chain for uranium-238

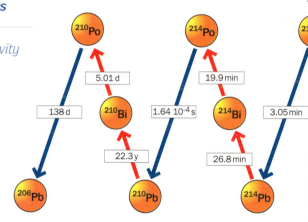

2
Concepts and quantities

Radioactivity and radiation

different form of beta decay: they lose positive charge through the emission of a *positron*, which is a positively charged electron.

The transformations often leave the nucleus with excess energy which it loses as *gamma rays* – high energy *photons* which are discrete parcels of energy without mass or charge.

These processes and similar ones are what we call *radioactivity*. The act of transformation is termed decay and the nuclide that changes and emits radiation is called a *radionuclide*.

Radioactivity and radiation

Although many nuclides are stable, most are not, stability being determined mainly by the number of neutrons and protons they contain. Smaller stable nuclei have about equal numbers: larger stable nuclei have more neutrons than protons. Nuclei with too many neutrons tend to transform themselves to a more stable structure by converting a neutron to a proton: this process, known as beta decay, involves the emission of a negatively charged electron called a *beta particle*. Nuclei with too many protons convert the excess protons to neutrons in a

Many radionuclides occur in nature. Most carbon, for instance, is in the form of carbon-12 with 6 protons and 6 neutrons and is completely stable. Interactions in the atmosphere with cosmic rays can, however, produce carbon-14, a radionuclide consisting of 6 protons and 8 neutrons. Carbon-14, with its extra neutrons, decays by changing a neutron to a proton and emitting a beta particle: in this way, the nuclide transforms to nitrogen-14, which consists of 7 protons and 7 neutrons. Measuring these decays in carbon-bearing materials is the basis of the technique of carbon dating.

Other naturally occurring radionuclides are formed in sequences or series of decays that

Molecule	Combined atoms
Atom	Nucleus + electrons
Nucleus	Protons + neutrons
Nuclide	Species of atom
Isotope	Equal number of protons

originate from the elements uranium and thorium. Each of these series ends with a stable nuclide of lead, but they also pass through radionuclides of other familiar elements. The diagram on p4 shows the decay series from uranium-238 ending in the stable nuclide lead-206: it passes through the radionuclide radon-222 which is of special significance in radiological protection. Some of the decays in the series, for example the decays of radium-226 and polonium-214, produce an *alpha particle* consisting of 2 protons and 2 neutrons. Identical with a nucleus of helium, the alpha particle is much heavier than the beta particle and carries two units of positive charge.

The energy of these forms of radiation – alpha and beta particles and gamma rays – is usually expressed in the unit of *electron volt*, symbol eV. Multiples of

this unit are often used such as a million or 10^6 electron volts, symbol MeV. For instance, the energy of alpha particles emitted by polonium-214 is about 7.7 MeV. Beta particles from lead-214, also formed in the uranium-238 decay series, have a maximum energy of 1.0 MeV, and gamma rays produced by it have energies up to 0.35 MeV.

During the past few decades, several hundred radioactive isotopes (radioisotopes) of natural elements have been produced artificially including, for example, strontium-90, caesium-137 and iodine-131. Several new radioactive elements have also been produced in quantity, for instance promethium and plutonium, although the latter does occur naturally in trace amounts in uranium ores.

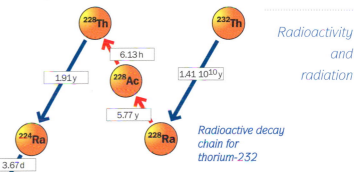

Radioactive decay chain for thorium-232

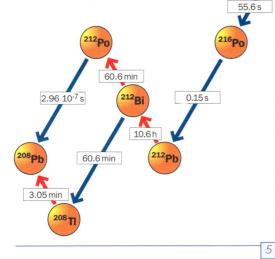

The rate at which spontaneous transformations occur in a given amount of a radioactive material is known as its *activity*. Activity is expressed in a unit called the becquerel, symbol Bq, where 1 Bq equals one transformation per second. As the unit is so small, multiples of the becquerel are frequently used, such as the megabecquerel, MBq, which is 1 million becquerels. One gram of plutonium-239, for instance, has an activity of approximately 2000 MBq: it emits about 2000 million alpha particles each second. The becquerel is named after the French physicist Henri Becquerel.

Henri Becquerel (1852–1908)

The time taken for the activity of a radionuclide to fall to half its original value is called the *half-life*, symbol $t^{1}/_2$; expressed otherwise, this is the time for half the nuclei in a sample to decay. Each radionuclide has a unique half-life:

iodine-131, 8 days;
caesium-137, 30 years;
carbon-14, 5730 years;
plutonium-239, 24 thousand years;
uranium-238, 4470 million years.

Values for various radionuclides range from fractions of a second to billions of years. In successive half-lives, the activity of a radionuclide is reduced by decay to $^{1}/_2$, $^{1}/_4$, $^{1}/_8$, $^{1}/_{16}$ and so on of its initial value. This means that we can predict the activity remaining at any future time. As the amount of a radionuclide decreases, the radiation emitted decreases proportionally.

Radionuclides	Unstable nuclides
Radioactivity	Emission of radiation
Radiations	α, β, γ, n, X-ray
Activity	Decay rate of radionuclide
Half-life	Time to half activity

Two other forms of radiation that require special mention are X-rays and neutrons (n). X-rays are usually produced by bombarding a metal target with electrons in a vacuum. They have properties similar to those of gamma rays but usually lower energies and so are less penetrating: an ordinary X-ray machine in a hospital emits X-rays with energies up to 0.15 MeV or so. Neutrons, a constituent of the nucleus, are produced in large numbers mainly in *nuclear reactors*, as discussed in Chapter 10.

Ionisation in matter

When radiation passes through matter, it deposits energy in the material concerned. Alpha and beta particles, being electrically charged, deposit energy through *electrical interactions* with electrons in the material. Gamma rays and X-rays lose energy in a variety of ways, but each involves liberating atomic (orbiting) electrons which then deposit energy in interactions with other electrons. Neutrons also lose energy in various ways, an important means being through collisions with hydrogen nuclei, which are single protons: the protons are set in motion and, being charged, they again deposit energy through electrical interactions. So in all cases, the radiation ultimately produces electrical interactions in the material.

In some cases, an electron in the material may receive enough energy to escape from an atom leaving the atom and the molecule thus formed positively charged. The figure illustrates this process for a molecule of water. The molecule has 10 protons altogether, but only 9 atomic electrons remain after a charged particle passes by; the molecule as a whole is thereby left with 1 excess positive charge.

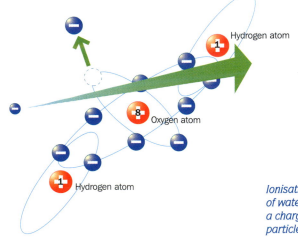

Ionisation of water by a charged particle

The process by which a neutral atom or molecule becomes charged is called *ionisation* and the resulting entity an *ion*. Once removed from an atom, an electron may in turn ionise other atoms or molecules. Any radiation that causes ionisation – either directly as with alpha and beta particles or indirectly as with gamma rays, X-rays, and neutrons – is known as ionising radiation. Charged particles passing through atoms may also give energy to the atomic electrons without actually removing them; this process is called *excitation*.

Ionisation in tissue

Each time a charged particle ionises or excites an atom, it loses energy until it no longer has enough energy to interact; the final result of these energy losses is to raise the temperature of the material minutely. In this way, all the energy deposited in biological tissues by ionising radiation is eventually dissipated as heat through increased vibrations of the atomic and molecular structures. It is the initial ionisation and the resulting chemical changes that cause harmful biological effects.

The basic unit of biological tissue is the cell, which has a control centre – as it were – called the nucleus. The *nucleus of a cell* is an intricate structure and not to be confused with the nucleus of an atom. About 80% of the cell consists of water, the other 20% being complex biological compounds.

When ionising radiation passes though cellular tissue, it produces charged water molecules. These break up into entities called *free radicals* such as the free hydroxyl radical OH composed of an oxygen atom and a hydrogen atom. Free radicals are highly reactive chemically and can alter important molecules in the cell.

One particularly important molecule is deoxyribonucleic acid, *DNA*, found mainly in the nucleus of the cell. DNA controls the structure and function of the cell and passes on copies of itself: its molecules are large and

2
**Concepts
and
quantities**

....

*Ionisation in
tissue*

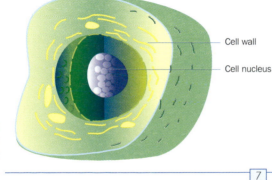

*A cell
and its
nucleus*

Cell wall

Cell nucleus

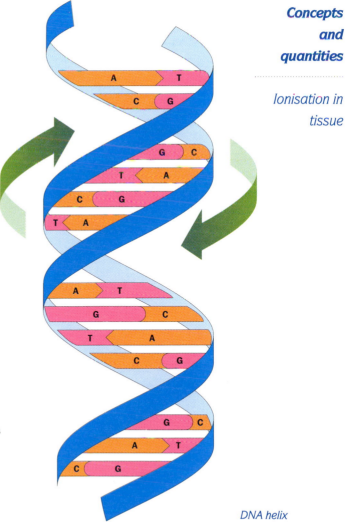

DNA helix

the structures that carry them, *chromosomes*, are visible through the microscope. We still do not fully understand the ways in which radiation damages cells but many involve changes to the DNA. There are two ways in which this can happen. Radiation may ionise a DNA molecule leading directly to a chemical change, or the DNA may be changed indirectly when it interacts with a free radical produced in the water of the cell by the radiation. In either case, the chemical change can cause a harmful biological effect leading to the development of cancers or inherited genetic defects. Chapter 4 has more detail on these matters.

2

Concepts and quantities

Dose quantities

Ionising radiation and tissue

Charged particles

▼

Electrical interactions

▼

Ionisation occurs

▼

Chemical changes

▼

Biological effects

A most important property of the various ionising radiations is their ability to penetrate matter. The depth of penetration for a particular type of radiation increases with energy but varies from one type of radiation to another for the same energy. With charged particles such as alpha and beta particles, the depth of penetration also depends on the mass of the particle and its charge: for equal energies, a beta particle will penetrate to a much greater depth than an alpha particle. Indeed alpha particles can scarcely penetrate the dead, outer layer of human skin; consequently, radionuclides that emit them are not hazardous unless they are

taken into the body through breathing or eating or through a skin wound. Beta particles may penetrate a centimetre or so of tissue, so radionuclides that emit them are hazardous to superficial tissues but not to internal organs unless they too are taken into the body. For indirectly ionising radiations such as gamma rays and neutrons, the degree of penetration depends on the nature of the interactions with tissue. Gamma rays can pass through the body, so radionuclides that emit them may be hazardous whether on the outside or the inside. X-rays and neutrons can also pass through the body.

Dose quantities

We cannot detect ionising radiations directly through our senses, but we can detect and measure them by other means: these include older methods based on *photographic films*, *Geiger–Müller tubes*, and *scintillation counters* as well as newer techniques using *thermoluminescent materials* and *silicon diodes*. We can interpret the measurements we make in terms of the energy that the radiation concerned would have deposited throughout the human body or in a particular part of the body. When direct measurements are not possible – when, for instance, a radionuclide is deposited in an internal organ – we can calculate the dose absorbed by that organ provided that we know the activity in the organ.

The amount of energy that ionising radiation deposits in a unit mass of matter, such as human tissue, is called the *absorbed dose*; it is expressed in a unit called the *gray*, symbol Gy, where 1 gray is equal to 1 joule per kilogram. Submultiples of the gray are

Harold Gray (1905–196

often used, such as the milligray, mGy, which is one-thousandth of a gray. The gray is named after the English physicist Harold Gray.

Ionising radiations differ in the way in which they interact with biological materials, so that equal absorbed doses (meaning equal amounts of energy deposited) do not necessarily have equal biological effects. For instance, 1 Gy to tissue from alpha radiation is more harmful than 1 Gy from beta radiation because an alpha particle, being slower and more heavily charged, loses its energy much more densely along its path. So in order to put all ionising radiations on an equal basis with regard to their potential for causing harm, we need another quantity. This is the *equivalent dose*. It is expressed in a unit called the *sievert*, symbol Sv.

Equivalent dose is equal to the absorbed dose multiplied by a factor that takes account of the way in which a particular radiation distributes energy in tissue so that we can allow for its relative effectiveness in causing biological harm. For gamma rays, X-rays, and beta particles, this radiation weighting factor is set at 1, so the absorbed dose and equivalent dose are numerically equal. For alpha particles, the factor is set at 20, so that the equivalent dose is deemed to be 20 times the absorbed dose. Values of the radiation weighting factor for neutrons of various energies range from 5 to 20. Submultiples of the sievert are commonly used, such as the millisievert, mSv, which is one-thousandth of a sievert. The sievert is named after the Swedish physicist Rolf Sievert.

Rolf Sievert (1896–1966)

Defined in this way, the equivalent dose provides an index of the risk of harm to a particular tissue or organ from exposure to various radiations regardless of their type or energy. So 1 Sv of alpha radiation to the lung, for example, would create the same risk of inducing fatal lung cancer as 1 Sv of beta radiation. The risk to the various parts of the human body varies from organ to organ: for example, the risk of fatal malignancy per unit equivalent dose is lower for the thyroid than for the lung. Moreover, there are other important types of harm such as non-fatal cancers or the risk of serious hereditary damage caused by irradiation of the testes or ovaries. These effects are different both in kind and in magnitude and we must take them into account when assessing the overall detriment to the health of human beings arising from exposure to radiation.

Tissue or organ	Tissue weighting factors
Gonads	0.20
Bone marrow (red)	0.12
Colon	0.12
Lung	0.12
Stomach	0.12
Bladder	0.05
Breast	0.05
Liver	0.05
Oesophagus	0.05
Thyroid	0.05
Skin	0.01
Bone surface	0.01
Remainder	0.05
Whole body total	**1.00**

We can deal with all these complexities by taking the equivalent dose in each of the major tissues and organs of the body and multiplying it by a weighting factor related to the risk associated with that tissue or organ. The sum of these weighted equivalent doses is a quantity called the *effective dose*: it allows us to represent the various dose equivalents in the body as a single number. Generally, the effective dose gives a broad indication of the detriment to health from any exposure to ionising radiation regardless of the energy and type of radiation; moreover, it applies equally to external and internal exposure and to uniform or non-uniform irradiation.

2
Concepts
and
quantities

Dose
quantities

Hierarchy of dose quantities

Absorbed dose
Energy imparted by radiation to unit mass of tissue

Equivalent dose
Absorbed dose weighted for harmfulness of different radiations

Effective dose
Equivalent dose weighted for susceptibility to harm of different tissues

Collective effective dose
Effective dose to a group from a source of radiation

It is sometimes useful to have a measure of the total radiation dose to groups of people or a whole population. The quantity used to express this total is the *collective effective dose*: it is obtained by summing over all groups the product of the average effective dose to the group from the radiation source of interest and the number of people in that group. For example, the effective dose from all sources of radiation is, on average, 2.6 mSv in a year to the inhabitants of the UK. Since the population of the UK is about

58 million, the collective effective dose to the whole community is the product of these two numbers – about 150 000 *man sievert*, symbol man Sv.

It is common for effective dose to be abbreviated to *dose* and collective effective dose to *collective dose*. This will be the case in the following chapters except where exactness is essential.

Calculation of effective dose

Consider a circumstance in which a radionuclide causes exposure of the lung, the liver, and the surfaces of the bones.

Suppose that the equivalent doses to the tissues are, respectively, 100, 70, and 300 mSv.

The effective dose is calculated as
$100 \times 0.12 + 70 \times 0.05 + 300 \times 0.01 = 18.5$ mSv

The calculation shows that the risk of harmful effects from this particular pattern of radiation exposure will be the same as the risk from 18.5 mSv received uniformly throughout the whole body.

---

3 Sources of ionising radiation

Ionising radiation enters our lives in a variety of ways. It arises from natural processes, such as the decay of uranium in the earth, and from artificial procedures, as with the use of X-rays in medicine. So we can classify radiation according to its origin. Natural sources include cosmic rays, gamma rays from the earth, radon *decay products* in the air, and various radionuclides in food and drink. Artificial sources include medical X-rays, *fallout* from the testing of nuclear weapons in the atmosphere, discharges of radioactive waste from the nuclear industry, industrial gamma rays, and miscellaneous items such as *consumer products*. Later chapters have more information on both classes of source.

Each source of radiation has two important characteristics, the dose that it delivers to human beings and the ease with which we can intervene to affect such doses. Until recently, radiation from natural sources seemed unremarkable and unalterable – a background phenomenon. We now know, however, that doses in the home from the decay products of radon gas (itself a product of uranium decay) can be remarkably high, although it is fairly easy to reduce them in existing homes and to avoid them when building new homes. By and large, we cannot change our exposure to the other natural sources: this basic background of cosmic rays, gamma rays, and natural radioactivity within the body gives rise to an annual dose around 1 mSv, on average, in the UK. A comparable dose from radon decay products is also un-avoidable, although it is important to eliminate exposure to the highest individual doses.

It is easier, in most cases, to control artificial sources of radiation because we can intervene to alter or terminate the procedure producing the radiation, but there is always a balance to be made. It would be unwise, for instance, to reduce doses from X-ray examinations if this were to lead to a loss of essential medical information.

NRPB regularly publishes data on doses from all sources: the results of the latest review are reflected in the piechart. The annual dose, averaged over the whole population, is about 2.6 mSv in total. Some 85% of this total is from natural sources with over half from radon decay products in the home. Medical exposure of patients accounts for 14% of the total, whereas all other artificial sources – fallout, consumer products, occupational exposure, and discharges from the nuclear industry – account for about 0.5% of the total value.

Contributions to average dose in the UK

3
Sources
of ionising
radiation

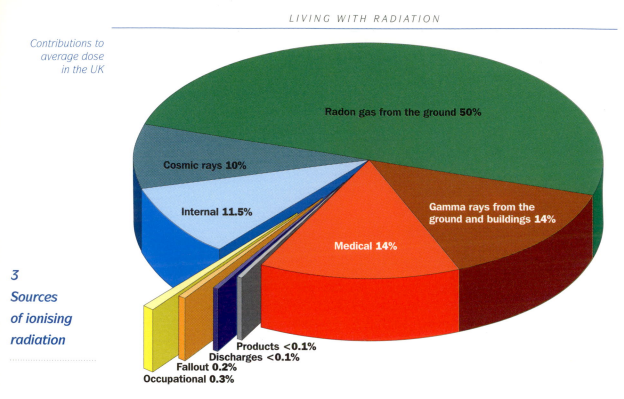

Radon gas from the ground 50%

Cosmic rays 10%

Internal 11.5%

Gamma rays from the ground and buildings 14%

Medical 14%

Products <0.1%
Discharges <0.1%
Fallout 0.2%
Occupational 0.3%

The greatest variations in dose arise from radon decay products in the home, which can give annual doses as high as 100 mSv. Annual doses at work are at present limited by law to 50 mSv, but in fact only about 1% of the workforce exceeds 15 mSv and almost all of the dose comes from exposure to radon in the workplace. It is unlikely that many members of the public receive more than a fraction of 1 mSv in a year from incidental exposure to artificial sources. Doses to patients in some diagnostic procedures may be around 10 mSv, but these are related to medical procedures. For consumer products that contain radioactive material, such as smoke alarms and luminous watches, annual doses are at most 1 µSv (1 millionth of a sievert), although thoriated gas mantles may cause as much as 0.1 mSv in a year in certain circumstances.

Average annual doses to the UK population from all sources of radiation	
SOURCE	DOSE (mSv)
Natural	
Cosmic	0.26
Gamma rays	0.35
Internal	0.3
Radon	1.3
Artificial	
Medical	0.37
Occupational	0.007
Fallout	0.005
Products	0.0004
Discharges	0.0002
Total (rounded)	**2.6**

4 Effects of ionising radiation

The effects of ionising radiation soon appear if a person receives a sufficient radiation dose. A very high dose to the whole body can cause death within a matter of weeks: for example, an absorbed dose of 5 Gy or more received instantaneously would probably be lethal, unless treatment were given, because of damage to the bone marrow and the gastrointestinal tract. If the same dose were instead restricted to a limited area of the body, it might not prove fatal but other early effects could occur: an instantaneous absorbed dose of 5 Gy or more to the skin would probably cause erythema within a week or so; higher doses would lead to more serious damage. Similar doses to the testes or ovaries might cause sterility.

If the same total dose were received over a period of weeks or months, there would be more opportunity for body cells to repair and there might be no early signs of injury.

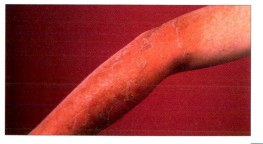

Erythemal damage to the skin

Even in the absence of early signs, however, tissues could still have been damaged with the effects becoming manifest only later in life or perhaps in the irradiated person's descendants. The most important of these late effects is cancer, which is always serious and frequently fatal.

Induction of cancers

Although the cause of most cancers remains unknown or poorly understood, exposures to agents such as tobacco smoke, asbestos, ultraviolet radiation, and ionising radiation are known to induce them. The development of cancer is a complex cellular process in several stages that usually takes many years. Radiation appears to act principally at the initiation stage by inducing certain mutations in the DNA of normal cells in tissues. These mutations allow a cell to enter a pathway of abnormal growth that can sometimes lead to the development of a malignancy.

In recent years, we have learned a great deal about the process by which radiation exposure leads to DNA damage and also about the cellular systems that act to repair or misrepair such damage and the mutations that may arise. Coupled with improved knowledge in cancer biology, this information provides supporting evidence for the long-standing belief that, although the risk of cancer after low doses of radiation may be very small, there is no dose – no matter how low – at which we can completely discount risk. We therefore assume the risk of cancer to increase in proportion with an increase in radiation dose.

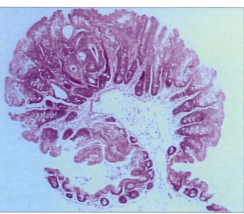

Early manifestation of a tumerous growth

4

Effects of ionising radiation

....

Risk assessments

These advances in knowledge also indicate that a person's genetic constitution influences the risk of cancer after irradiation. At present, we can identify only rare families who may carry increased risk, but experts may in future be able to take some account of such inherited traits in radiological protection practice.

How can we calculate the *risk* of cancer from exposure to radiation? Suppose that we know the number of people in an irradiated group and the doses they have received. Then by observing the occurrence of cancer in the group and analysing it in relation to the doses and the number of cancers expected in an otherwise similar but unirradiated group, we can estimate the raised risk of cancer per unit dose; this is commonly called a *risk factor*. It is most important to include data for large groups of people in these calculations so as to minimise the statistical uncertainties in the estimates and take account of factors, such as

age and gender, that affect the spontaneous development of cancer.

Not all cancers are fatal. Mortality from radiation-induced thyroid cancer is about 10%, from breast cancer about 50%, and from skin cancer about 1%. Overall, the risk of inducing cancer by uniformly irradiating the whole body is about half as great again as the risk of inducing a fatal cancer. In radiological protection the risk of fatal cancer is of more concern because of its extreme significance. The use of fatal cancer risks also makes it easier to compare them with the other fatal risks encountered in life; in contrast, comparisons of non-fatal risks are fraught with difficulty.

Risk assessments

The main source of information on the additional risk of cancer following exposure of the whole body to gamma radiation comes from studies on the survivors of the *atomic bombs* dropped at Hiroshima and Nagasaki in 1945. Other risk estimates for the exposure of various tissues and organs to X-rays and gamma rays come from people exposed to external radiation for the treatment of non-malignant or malignant conditions and for diagnostic purposes and also from people in the Marshall Islands exposed to severe fallout from atmospheric *nuclear weapons* tests. Information on the effects of alpha-emitting radionuclides comes from miners exposed to radon and its decay products, from workers exposed to radium-226 in luminous paint, from some patients treated with radium-224 for bone disease, and from other patients given an X-ray contrast medium containing thorium oxide.

Information of this nature is assessed periodically by the United Nations Scientific Committee on the Effects of Atomic Radiation

(UNSCEAR), the International Commission on Radiological Protection (ICRP), the US National Academy of Sciences Committee on the Biological Effects of Ionizing Radiation (BEIR Committee), and by NRPB. Such assessments yield estimates of risk that are heavily dependent on data from the Life Span Study of the atomic bomb survivors as supplemented by data from the other study groups. Since a substantial proportion of those who survived the bombings in 1945 is still alive more than five decades later, it is necessary to predict how many excess cancers will have been found by the time all the survivors have died. Various mathematical methods are used for this purpose; the process introduces some uncertainty in the risk estimates.

Risk factors for cancers

Cancer risks derived from the Japanese atomic bomb survivors and other exposed groups are based largely on high doses received during short periods. In ordinary circumstances, most people are exposed to low levels of radiation throughout long periods. The central assumption in radiological protection is that there is a proportional relationship between dose and risk. For some highly ionising radiations, such as alpha particles, the relationship is directly proportional or linear. In contrast, with sparsely ionising radiations such as gamma rays, for example, there is considerable evidence from the study of *radiobiology* that the risk is less at low doses and low dose rates than is implied by linear interpolation from high doses and high dose rates.

The position is illustrated in the diagram where the data points are at high levels. Curve A shows the likely nature of the relationship between dose and risk and curve B shows how a direct interpolation would lead to an

overestimate of the risk at low levels. Curve C, which is extrapolated from the slope of curve A at low levels, gives the best indication of the relationship between dose and risk for ordinary circumstances of exposure to gamma rays. In short, the ratio of the slopes of B and C is the reduction factor that must be applied to the original data to get the appropriate risk factor.

ICRP has estimated the risk factors for fatal cancers in this way using a judicious reduction factor of 2. The calculations are for a representative international population based on the characteristics of five disparate national populations.

The estimates, usually given in scientific notation, may be expressed in other ways: $5.0 \times 10^{-2}\,\text{Sv}^{-1}$, for example, is the same as 5% per Sv or 1 in 20 per Sv. This is the life-time risk of contracting fatal cancer from unit cumulative dose of radiation. The risk factor

4

Effects of

ionising

radiation

Risk

factors for

cancers

Relationship between dose and risk

ICRP risk factors for fatal cancers	
TISSUE OR ORGAN	RISK FACTOR ($\times 10^{-2}\,Sv^{-1}$)
Bladder	0.30
Bone marrow (red)	0.50
Bone surface	0.05
Breast	0.20
Colon	0.85
Liver	0.15
Lung	0.85
Oesophagus	0.30
Ovary	0.10
Skin	0.02
Stomach	1.10
Thyroid	0.08
Remainder	0.50
Total (rounded)	**5.00**

4

Effects of ionising radiation

....

Hereditary disease

for the working population (those aged 18 to 65 years) is lower because it does not contain children and young people who have more years at risk after exposure: the total value for workers is $4.0 \times 10^{-2}\,Sv^{-1}$ or 4% per Sv.

Values of the risk factors apply to typical people in a population regardless of age or gender: for an actual person, however, they depend both on age and on gender. If a person receives a dose late in life, a cancer may not have time to appear before the person dies of another cause; and the risk of breast cancer is virtually zero for men and twice the listed value, $0.4 \times 10^{-2}\,Sv^{-1}$ or 1 in 250, for women.

A crucial characteristic of the representative international population is the prevailing risk of fatal cancer from all causes because the risk from radiation is related to it. Since cancer mortality in the UK is generally somewhat higher than worldwide, the risk factors are as much as 25% above the ICRP risk estimates but within the uncertainty.

Hereditary disease

Apart from cancer, the other main late effect of radiation is hereditary disease. As with cancer, the *probability* of hereditary disease – but not its severity – depends on dose. Genetic damage arises from irradiation of the testes and ovaries, which produce sperm cells in males and the egg cells in females. Ionising radiation can induce *mutations* in these cells or in the germ cells that form them, mutations which may give rise to harmful effects in future generations. Mutations occur as a result of structural changes to the DNA in single germ cells, which subsequently carry the hereditary information in the DNA through future generations. The hereditary diseases that may be caused vary in severity ranging from early death and serious mental defects to relatively trivial skeletal abnormalities and minor metabolic disorders.

Although mutations appear to arise in human beings without any apparent cause, natural radiation and other agents in the environment may also cause them and contribute to the prevailing occurrence of hereditary disease. There has, however, been no conclusive evidence in human offspring for hereditary defects attributable to exposure from natural or artificial radiation. Extensive studies of the offspring of the survivors of the atomic bombs, in particular, have failed to show increases of statistical significance in hereditary defects; instead, the negative findings help to provide an upper estimate of the risk factor for them.

Large experimental studies have been made of the hereditary damage that ionising radiation induces in animals, mainly mice. These have covered a wide range of doses and dose rates and clearly demonstrate that ionising radiation does cause mutations. The results also show how often hereditary defects are induced by known doses. When considered with the findings for the atomic bomb survivors, this information allows estimates to be made of the hereditary risk for human beings.

Against this background, ICRP has assessed the risk of severe hereditary disease in a general population of all ages exposed to low doses and dose rates. It estimated a risk factor of $1.0 \times 10^{-2} \, Sv^{-1}$ or 1 in 100 per Sv for such diseases appearing at any time in all future generations. Mutations leading to diseases that are strictly heritable, such as haemophilia and Down's Syndrome, make up about half of the total: the remainder comes from a group of so-called multifactorial diseases such as diabetes and asthma. This estimate of risk carries considerable uncertainty especially for the multifactorial diseases where the interplay of the genetic and environmental factors that influence the disorders is poorly understood.

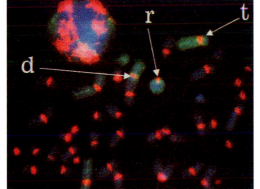

In genetic terms, irradiation of the testes and ovaries is potentially harmful only if it occurs before or during the reproductive period of life: for people who will not subsequently have children there is, of course, no hereditary risk. Since the proportion of a working population that is likely to reproduce is lower than that in the general population, the risk factor for workers is smaller: ICRP estimates $0.6 \times 10^{-2} \, Sv^{-1}$ or 1 in 170 per Sv for severe hereditary diseases in all future generations.

Communal risk

An important consequence of the assumption that risk is proportional to dose, without a low dose threshold, is that the collective effective dose becomes an indicator of communal harm. It makes no difference mathematically whether, in a community of 50 000 people, each receives an effective dose of 2 mSv, or in a community of 20 000 people, each receives 5 mSv; the collective dose in each community is 100 man Sv, and the communal cost in each community may be five cancer deaths and one severe hereditary defect in future generations. Members of the smaller community, however, run the greater *individual* risk of fatal cancer. Calculations of collective dose should not be taken too far: the product of an infinitude of people and an infinitesimal dose, with the calculation of expected numbers of cancer deaths, is likely to be meaningless.

Other late effects

One category of late effects does not involve an element of probability: these effects will appear in people if they receive a large dose over a long time, and the severity will increase with increasing dose. Such effects are not usually fatal but can be disabling or distressing because the function of some parts of the body may be impaired or other non-malignant changes may arise. The best known examples are cataracts (opacity in the lens of the eye) and skin damage (thinning and ulceration). High absorbed doses of several gray are normally required to induce these conditions.

Irradiation in pregnancy

The risks to children irradiated while in the womb deserve special mention. If an embryo or fetus is exposed to radiation at the time when organs are forming, developmental defects such as a reduced diameter of the head or mental retardation may be caused.

Studies on survivors of the atomic bombs who were exposed before birth have indicated that mental retardation mainly follows exposure during the period between 8 and 15 weeks after conception. There has been debate over the form of the relationship between dose and response and the existence of a threshold below which there is no effect. For exposures during the most sensitive 8–15 week period, however, ICRP assumes that the decrease in IQ depends directly on the dose without a threshold and with a loss of 30 IQ points per Sv. So, for example, exposure of the fetus to 5 mSv during this stage of pregnancy would lead to a loss in IQ of 0.15 point, which would be undetectable.

High doses to the embryo and fetus can cause death or gross malformation: the threshold for these effects is between 0.1 Sv and 1 Sv or more depending on the time after conception. Genetic risks to fetuses are judged to be the same as those for a fully reproductive population after birth, namely $2.4 \times 10^{-2}\,Sv^{-1}$ or 1 in 40 per Sv. Irradiation before birth can also lead to an increased risk of malignancy in childhood. The risk of fatal cancer up to age 15 years is estimated to be about $3.0 \times 10^{-2}\,Sv^{-1}$ or 1 in 30 per Sv, and the overall risk of cancer about twice this value.

For all of these reasons it is best for pregnant women to avoid diagnostic X-rays of the abdomen unless a delay until the end of pregnancy would be undesirable. Indeed for all women of reproductive age where pregnancy cannot be reasonably excluded, it may be prudent to restrict diagnostic procedures that give high doses in the pelvic area to the early part of the menstrual cycle when pregnancy is least likely. Special restrictions apply to the doses that pregnant women may receive if they are employed in work with radiation sources.

4

Effects of ionising radiation

....

Irradiation in pregnancy

Harmful radiation effects

HEALTH CONSEQUENCES	CIRCUMSTANCES OF EXPOSURE	SOURCES OF INFORMATION
Early effects		
	High dose and dose rate:	Human data from various sources
Death	to much of the body	
Erythema	to area of skin	
Sterility	to testes and ovaries	
Late effects		
Various cancers	Any dose or dose rate	Risk factors for human beings
	Risk depends on dose	estimated from high doses and
	Appear years later	dose rates in human health studies
Hereditary defects	Any dose or dose rate	Risk factors for human beings
	Risk depends on dose	inferrred from animal data and
	Appear in offspring	the absence of human evidence
Functional damage	High dose at any rate	Human data from various sources
to organs and tissues	Various times to appear	
Mental retardation	Dose in the womb	Limited human data
	Appears in the child	

5 System of radiological protection

General principles

Approaches to protection against ionising radiation are remarkably consistent throughout the world. This is due largely to the International Commission on Radiological Protection (ICRP), the non-governmental scientific organisation that for seven decades or so has published recommendations for protection against ionising radiations.
Its authority derives from the scientific standing of its members and the merit of its recommendations. Governments adopt the recommendations and put them into practice in a manner appropriate to the countries concerned. The European Commission undertakes a similar task for member states of the European Union with the aim of producing a harmonised approach to radiological protection mainly through binding directives.

For all human actions or practices that add to radiation exposure, ICRP recommends a system of radiological protection based on three central requirements. Each of these involves social considerations – explicitly in the first two and implicitly in the third – so there is considerable need for the exercise of judgement.

In some cases, as for example after an accident that releases radioactive material to the

5
System of
radiological
protection

....

General
principles

ICRP system of radiological protection for practices

1 JUSTIFICATION OF A PRACTICE
No practice involving exposures to radiation should be adopted unless it produces at least sufficient benefit to the exposed individuals or to society to offset the radiation detriment it causes

2 OPTIMISATION OF PROTECTION
In relation to any particular source of radiation within a practice, all reasonable steps should be taken to adjust the protection so as to maximise the net benefit, economic and social factors being taken into account

3 APPLICATION OF INDIVIDUAL DOSE LIMITS
A limit should be applied to the dose, other than from medical exposures, received by any individual as the result of all the practices to which he or she is exposed

---

environment or when high indoor levels of radon occur, it may be necessary to intervene to reduce the exposure of people. Under such circumstances, ICRP recommends a system of radiological protection for intervention based on two further principles which mainly differ from the first set in that they omit dose limits: specifying limits might require measures out of all proportion to the likely benefit and would therefore be in conflict with the first principle. The application of this system again requires the exercise of judgement.

> **ICRP system of radiological protection for intervention**
>
> **1** The proposed intervention should do more good than harm, that is, the benefits resulting from the reduction in dose should be sufficient to justify the harm and the costs, including social costs, of the intervention
>
> **2** The form, scale, and duration of the intervention should be chosen so that the net benefit of the reduction of dose, that is, the benefit of the reduction in dose less the costs of the intervention, should be as large as reasonably achievable

5
System of radiological protection

Justification of practices

NRPB has endorsed both systems of radiological protection for use in the UK. In this chapter, we shall concentrate mainly on the system of protection for practices: in later chapters, we shall discuss circumstances in which intervention may be necessary.

Scope of application
We can generally do nothing sensible to reduce the normal levels of dose from natural radiation, although it is appropriate to intervene when people are exposed to high levels of radon in their homes. For workers, however, some control needs to be exercised over exposures to sources of natural radiation. Three sources are particularly important: radon in mines and other places, cosmic rays on-board aircraft, and ores with elevated levels of natural activity.

The use of radiation in medicine is mainly a matter of clinical judgement since medical exposures are intended to benefit patients. Setting limits on doses to patients would not be sensible: it might also limit the benefits. However, the principles of justification and optimisation, discussed next, should apply in full, particularly as the collective dose from medical procedures is high.

Justification of practices
The first requirement in the system of radiological protection for practices emphasises the obvious need to consider harmful costs in the light of any benefits. In most cases, radiation effects are just some of a number of possible harmful outcomes that make up part of the overall social and economic costs. If there are other ways to achieve the same end, with or without radiation, it is important to analyse the costs and benefits of the alternatives before making a final decision.

The issues that arise in the process of justification extend beyond radiological protection and may be illustrated by the arguments about the *nuclear power* programme. The radiological consequences of the programme include the discharge of radioactive substances to the environment and the doses received by workers in the *nuclear power industry*. In addition, a full analysis would deal with the potential for nuclear reactor accidents as well as the creation of highly *radioactive wastes*. Account should also be taken of doses and accidents to overseas uranium miners.

An assessment should then be made of the consequences of doing without the energy provided by nuclear power or of using alternative methods to produce it – with coal for instance. Generating electric power from coal creates large volumes of waste and releases gases that worsen the greenhouse effect. Coal-fired power stations also discharge other noxious substances including natural radioactivity, miners suffer occupational disease, and there is the potential for mining accidents. A complete analysis would also need to consider several strategic and economic factors: the diversity, security, availability, and reserves of various fuels; the construction and operating costs of various types of power station; the expected demand for electricity; the willingness of people to work in a particular industry.

Proper justification is also required for the use of X-rays in diagnostic medicine. Few of us would question the practice: the benefits are undoubted even though individual doses for some examinations, and collective doses generally, are high. Nevertheless each procedure needs to be judged on its own merits: a mass X-ray screening programme for cancer that might cause more cancers than it was likely to reveal would clearly be unacceptable. For this reason, there is unlikely to be clinical justification for the routine screening of employees except in special circumstances such as the prevention of tuberculosis. Medical irradiation during pregnancy requires clear justification and careful techniques. Radiological examinations for legal or insurance purposes are usually unwarranted since they do not benefit the health of the exposed person.

Practices are proposed from time to time that fail to satisfy the test of justification: these include the production of toys and jewellery containing radioactive material and other devices such as security tags for which there are non-radioactive alternatives.

Optimisation of protection

Since we must assume that no radiation dose is entirely free from risk, it is not enough merely to comply with a dose limit: it is important to pay attention to doses below the limit and to reduce them whenever it is reasonably achievable. Of course eventually the point must come when further reductions in dose become unreasonable in the sense that the social and economic costs would outweigh the value of the reductions.

As for the second requirement – the optimisation of protection – we need to note here that ICRP has seen fit to place a constraint on the procedure. This takes the form of restrictions on doses or risks to people so as to prevent inequitable exposures from radiation.

Optimisation of protection has been increasingly influential during the past two decades with the result that the annual dose to radiation workers in the UK has fallen to 1.5 mSv, on average, an *order of magnitude* below the dose limit for a single year of 20 mSv that NRPB has recommended. Some groups of workers receive doses a few times the average, and some workers receive more than 20 mSv in a year, but the number doing so is a very small percentage of the total. Exposure to natural sources of radiation in the workplace affects the national average appreciably: occupational exposure to artificial sources alone leads to an average annual dose of 0.3 mSv.

The annual doses to individual members of the public from practices that cause exposure have been brought below the limit of 1 mSv in a single year recommended by NRPB. The small groups of people who are most exposed to radioactive discharges from nuclear facilities typically receive 0.14 mSv in a year, but a few individuals may receive as much as 0.5 mSv in a year by direct irradiation near some nuclear power stations.

There are a number of reasons for these achievements. Since managements must keep doses from practices below certain limits, average doses will tend to be lower still. Moreover, dose constraints are increasingly being used: based on experience gained from well-managed operations, these may be set appreciably below the dose limit. Practices that cause exposure of the public are controlled through cautious estimates of the dose to the most highly exposed group of individuals and the application of an appropriate constraint. All such procedures are judicious ways of fulfilling the requirement to keep all doses as low as reasonably achievable.

5

System of radiological protection

....

Constraints

Limitation of doses

The third requirement for practices expresses the obligation not to expose individual people and their descendants to an unacceptable degree of risk. This is fulfilled by imposing strict dose limits and adopting constraints. At the time of writing, the statutory limit for workers is still 50 mSv in a year, but following the latest ICRP recommendations, NRPB advises that it should be reduced to 20 mSv in a year.

NRPB dose limits and constraints (mSv y^{-1})		
PARAMETERS	WORKERS	PUBLIC
Effective dose		
Prime limit	20[a]	1
Constraint	15[b]	0.3[c]
Equivalent dose		
Lens of eye	150[a]	15
Area of skin[d]	500[a]	50
Extremities[e]	500[a]	50

NOTES

(a) For students and apprentices, three-tenths of these values.

(b) Maximum value.

(c) Prospective value for a single new source of exposure.

(d) Averaged over any 1 cm^2 of skin regardless of area exposed.

(e) Forearms and ankles as well as hands and feet.

For a member of the public, the statutory limit is 5 mSv in a year: NRPB advises that this should be reduced to 1 mSv in a year.

These prime limits, expressed in terms of effective dose, are intended to control the incidence of serious effects such as cancer and hereditary harm that involve an element of probability. Another set of limits, expressed in terms of equivalent dose, is to protect the eyes, skin and extremities against other forms of damage. Both sets are virtually identical with those of ICRP, as is the recommendation that the dose to the fetus of a pregnant worker should not exceed 1 mSv once pregnancy has been declared.

There are two common misconceptions about dose limits. The first is that they mark an abrupt change in biological risk, a line of demarcation between safe and unsafe. It should be clear from the discussion on dose and risk that this is not so: it should also be apparent from the fact that there are different dose limits for workers and members of the public. These limits differ because higher risks are deemed more acceptable for workers, who receive a benefit from their employment, than for members of the public, whose risk is involuntary. The second misconception is that keeping doses below the limits is the only important requirement in radiological protection: on the contrary, the overriding requirement is to keep doses as low as reasonably achievable. There is an increasing emphasis on dose constraints, which are, of course, set below dose limits.

Constraints

Constraints are best imposed on a practice involving exposure to radiation at the planning stage. For workers, the annual value of dose should be chosen so as to reflect what can reasonably be reached in a particular industry or procedure; it may well be a small fraction of the dose limit. NRPB recommends a maximum value of 15 mSv in a year, which is also to be regarded as an investigation level for doses already incurred from existing practices. For members of the public, the NRPB constraint, 0.3 mSv in a year, is a planning value for a new source of radiation exposure such as a factory that intends to discharge radioactive material to the environment.

A form of dose constraint is also appropriate for medical exposures of patients. In this circumstance, however, the parameter is called a reference dose even though the object is still to minimise doses in a sensible way. We shall return to this topic in Chapter 7.

Comparing risks

One way of judging the effectiveness of the system of radiological protection is to compare the residual risks of fatal cancer from radiation with the prevailing risks of death from other causes. Two circumstances are relevant – risks at work and risks otherwise.

To facilitate comparison, it is helpful to consider what levels of risk might be appropriate in an advanced country such as the UK. The simple diagram shows how risk alters from being low and acceptable through a tier of tolerability into a high region of unacceptability. Assessments by the Royal Society and other organisations indicate that a fatal risk of 10^{-3} or 1 in 1000 in a year is about the limit of tolerability for workers: for members of the general public, however, a fatal risk around 10^{-5} or 1 in 100 000 in a year is judged to be near the limit. An important reason for the difference is that workers are exposed voluntarily to the radiation risk, whereas members of the general public are likely to have it imposed on them.

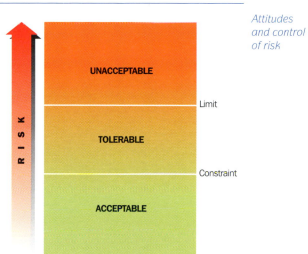

The annual risk of fatal cancer associated with the annual average dose of 1.5 mSv for workers is 6.0×10^{-5} or 1 in 17 000; it is appreciably higher than the general level of fatal accidents in the manufacturing and service sectors and comparable to the risk in the construction industry. Although such comparisons are inherently cautious because the nature and time of death are so different, there can be no dispute about the end effect; it must be noted that radiation workers also run the risk of death from conventional causes. Comparative data show why continuous exposure at 20 mSv in a year would be undesirable: the implied risk of fatal cancer is 8.0×10^{-4} or 1 in 1250.

Average annual risk of death in the UK from industrial accidents and from cancers due to radiation work		
Coal mining	1.4×10^{-4}	1 in 7000
Oil and gas extraction	1.3×10^{-4}	1 in 8000
Construction	6.3×10^{-5}	1 in 16000
Radiation work (1.5 mSv y^{-1})	6.0×10^{-5}	1 in 17000
Metal manufacture	2.9×10^{-5}	1 in 34000
All manufacture	1.1×10^{-5}	1 in 90000
Chemical production	1.0×10^{-5}	1 in 100000
All services	4.5×10^{-6}	1 in 220000

Average annual risk of death in the UK from some common causes		
Smoking 10 cigarettes a day	5.0×10^{-3}	1 in 200
Heart disease	3.3×10^{-3}	1 in 300
All cancers	2.5×10^{-3}	1 in 400
All causes, 40 years old	1.4×10^{-3}	1 in 700
All radiation ($2.6\,\mathrm{mSv}\,\mathrm{y}^{-1}$)	1.3×10^{-4}	1 in 7700
Accident in the home	6.9×10^{-5}	1 in 15000
Accident on the road	5.9×10^{-5}	1 in 17000
Homicide	1.0×10^{-5}	1 in 100000
Nuclear discharges ($0.14\,\mathrm{mSv}\,\mathrm{y}^{-1}$)	7.0×10^{-6}	1 in 140000
Pregnancy, for mother	6.0×10^{-6}	1 in 170000

on the Health and Safety Executive (HSE). Several government departments and the agencies they sponsor also have important rôles: the Department of Health has a particular interest in radiological protection through its sponsorship of NRPB.

Links with other organisat

5
System of radiological protection

Legal controls

The annual risk of fatal cancer associated with the average annual dose of 2.6 mSv to the public in the UK from all sources of radiation is about 1.3×10^{-4} or 1 in 7700. Most of this is attributable to natural sources about which we can do little. Some members of the public are particularly concerned about the risks from nuclear discharges: as the data show, however, the annual risk to the most exposed group is about 7.0×10^{-6} or 1 in 140000 – much the same as the risk of death during pregnancy. Since the risk of fatal cancer associated with the dose limit of 1 mSv in a year is about 5.0×10^{-5} or 1 in 20000, it is clear why constraints are required.

Legal controls

The system of radiological protection described here is implemented by statute in the UK. A substantial body of legislation has built up since the 1940s and is supported by codes of good practice and advisory material; there is also a comprehensive scheme of licences, authorisations, and approvals. Virtually every circumstance is covered from the design of nuclear power stations through the control of radon in offices to the use of X-ray sets in veterinary surgeries.

Responsibility for enforcing radiological protection in workplaces in the UK falls mainly

As a member of the European Union, the UK is obliged to implement various directives on radiological protection formulated by the European Commission and made by the Council of Ministers. As indicated previously, such directives are closely derived from the recommendations of ICRP and are compatible with systems of control in most advanced countries throughout the world. Developments during the past four decades have been in the direction of more stringent controls as more information on risks has become available.

NRPB contributes to the development of the ICRP recommendations and the consultations on the European Commission directives and then advises on their applicability in the UK.

6 Natural ionising radiation

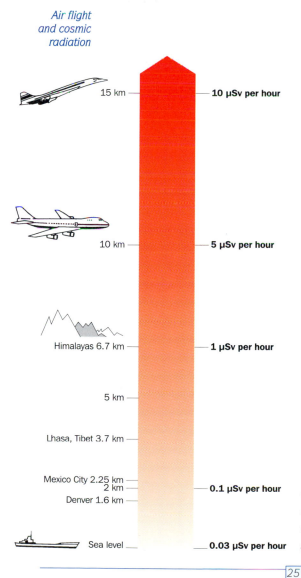

Air flight and cosmic radiation

15 km	**10 µSv per hour**
10 km	**5 µSv per hour**
Himalayas 6.7 km	**1 µSv per hour**
5 km	
Lhasa, Tibet 3.7 km	
Mexico City 2.25 km	
2 km	**0.1 µSv per hour**
Denver 1.6 km	
Sea level	**0.03 µSv per hour**

Natural ionising radiation pervades the whole environment. Cosmic rays reach the earth from outer space, the earth itself is radioactive, and natural activity is present in food and drink and in the air. We are all exposed to natural radiation to a greater or lesser extent, and for most people it is the major source of radiation exposure. Nevertheless, animals and plants have evolved in this background of natural radiation, and the general view is that it is not a significant risk to health – but there are exceptions.

Cosmic radiation

Cosmic rays are mainly protons of uncertain origin in space and very high energies which reach our atmosphere in fairly constant numbers. It is known, however, that some protons with lower energies come from the sun and are given off in bursts during solar flares. Protons are charged particles, so the number entering the atmosphere is affected by the earth's magnetic field: more come in near the poles than the equator. As they penetrate the atmosphere, the cosmic rays initiate complex reactions and are gradually absorbed so that the dose decreases as altitude decreases. In the UK, the annual effective dose equivalent from cosmic rays at ground level is about 0.25 mSv, on average.

Most people in the UK live at low altitudes, so there is little variation in annual dose on this account; nor is there much variation with latitude. The type of building in which a person lives may affect the dose to a slight degree. The intensity of cosmic rays at altitudes where aircraft fly is much greater than on the ground. General air travel gives rise to a further annual dose of 0.01 mSv, on average, bringing the total to 0.26 mSv.

Gamma radiation

All materials in the earth's crust contain radioactive species: indeed energy from natural activity deep in the earth contributes to the shaping of the crust. This energy comes mainly from uranium, thorium, and potassium.

Uranium is dispersed throughout rocks and soils in low concentrations of a few parts per million (ppm); where it exceeds 1000 ppm or so in an ore, it may be economical to mine for use in nuclear reactors. As we have seen, uranium-238 is the parent of a long series of radionuclides of several elements, which decay in succession until the stable nuclide lead-206 is reached. Among the decay products in the series is an isotope of the radioactive gas radon, namely radon-222, which can reach the atmosphere, where it continues to decay. Thorium is similarly dispersed in the earth, and thorium-232 is the parent of another radioactive series, which gives rise to radon-220, another isotope of radon, sometimes called thoron. Potassium is far more common than either uranium or thorium and makes up 2.4% by weight of the earth's crust. The radionuclide potassium-40, however, constitutes only 120 ppm of stable potassium.

The radionuclides in the earth emit penetrating gamma rays that irradiate us more or less uniformly. Since building materials are extracted from the earth, they too are mildly radioactive, and people are irradiated indoors as well as out of doors. The doses they receive are affected both by the geology of the area where they live and the structure of the buildings in which they live, but the average effective dose in the UK from natural gamma rays is about 0.35 mSv in a year. Actual values vary appreciably: some people may receive doses a few times higher or lower than the average. Although there is little that can be done to affect this dose, it would be sensible to avoid building sites and materials with unusually high activity.

Annual effective doses in the UK from natural radiation		
	Dose (mSv)	
Source	Average	Broad range
Cosmic radiation	0.26	0.2–0.3
Gamma radiation	0.35	0.1–1.0
Radon inhalation	1.3	0.3–100
Internal irradiation	0.3	0.1–1.0
Total (rounded)	**2.2**	**1.0–100**

Radon inhalation

Radon gas is a particularly significant source of exposure to natural radiation. This is because the immediate decay products of radon-222 are radionuclides with short half-lives which attach themselves to fine particles in the air, are inhaled, irradiate the tissues of the lung with alpha particles, and increase the risk of lung cancer. The same is true of radon-220, but the degree of exposure of the lung is much less. When radon gas enters the atmosphere from the ground, it disperses in the air, so concentrations out of doors are low. When the gas enters a building, predominantly through the floor from the ground, the concentration of activity builds up within the enclosed space: for the UK, it is typically about 20 Bq m^{-3} (becquerel per cubic metre of air).

The annual effective dose in the UK from the decay products of radon is estimated to be 1.3 mSv, on average. There are, however, pronounced variations about this value: in some homes, the occupants have received doses two orders of magnitude higher. Areas affected by radon to a marked degree have been identified throughout the UK.

If the radon level exceeds 200 Bq m^{-3}, ten times the average, homeowners are advised to reduce it so as to reduce the risk of lung cancer; this concentration is known as the Action Level. Anyone finding such a high radon level can reduce it by preventing air from the ground entering the building. The most effective way to do so is to reduce the air pressure under the house with a small fan. In the most affected areas, the building regulations have been changed to ensure that new homes do not have high radon levels.

As mentioned in Chapter 5, this circumstance is an example of intervention, in the ICRP sense, to reduce human exposure to ionising radiation.

Internal irradiation

Other radionuclides from the uranium and thorium series, in particular lead-210 and polonium-210, are present in air, food, and water, and so irradiate the body internally. Potassium-40 also comes into the body with the normal diet; it is the main source of internal irradiation apart from the radon decay products. In addition, the interactions of cosmic rays with the atmosphere create a number of radionuclides, such as carbon-14, which also contribute to internal irradiation.

The average effective dose from these sources of internal irradiation is estimated to be 0.3 mSv in a year for the UK with potassium-40

6
Natural
ionising
radiation
....
Internal
irradiation

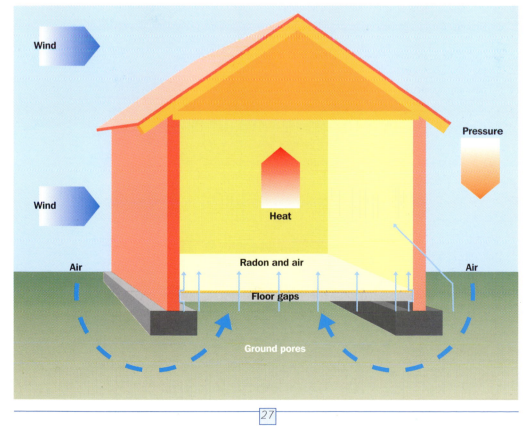

Wind

Wind

Pressure

Heat

Radon and air

Air

Air

Floor gaps

Ground pores

*Radon
in homes*

contributing about half. Information on how the total varies from one person to another is limited, although it is known that the potassium content of the human body is controlled by biological processes: the amount of potassium, and hence potassium-40, varies with the amount of muscle in the body, and is about twice as high in young men as in older women. There is little anyone could do to affect internal irradiation from the other radionuclides except by avoiding any food and water with a high radioactive content.

Total doses

The total average effective dose from natural radiation is about 2.2 mSv in a year for the UK. Differences in average doses from one locality to another readily exceed 10 mSv in a year, and differences in individual doses may exceed 100 mSv in a year because of homes with particularly high levels of radon and its decay products. The collective effective dose is about 130 000 man Sv in a year.

Collective and individual doses are useful measures for comparing the significance for health of natural and artificial radiations, but they may need to be supplemented by additional data when there are, as with indoor radon, large variations about the average. The most helpful step might be to describe the frequency with which doses of a certain magnitude occur in the circumstances of interest.

7 Medical uses of ionising radiation

7

**Medical
uses of
ionising
radiation**

*Diagnostic
radiology*

Ionising radiation has two very different uses in medicine – for diagnosis and therapy. Both are intended to benefit patients and, as with any use of radiation, the benefit must outweigh the risk. We have touched on this matter of justification in Chapter 5.

Most people at some time in their lives have an X-ray examination to help the physician diagnose disease or damage in the body. A much less common diagnostic procedure involves the administration of radionuclides to patients so as to observe how organs are functioning. Physicians use either of these procedures if they cannot make a diagnosis without them. Radiation doses are generally low although they can be appreciable in certain procedures.

Much higher doses are required to treat malignant diseases or malfunctioning organs sometimes in combination with other forms of treatment. A beam of radiation may be used to irradiate the affected part of the body or a fairly high activity of a radionuclide may be administered to the patient.

The use of X-rays for examining patients is called *diagnostic radiology* and the use of radionuclides for diagnosis or therapy *nuclear medicine*. When radiation beams are used to treat patients, the procedure is called *radiotherapy*.

Diagnostic radiology

In a conventional X-ray examination, radiation from a machine passes through the patient. X-rays penetrate flesh and bone to different degrees and produce images on photographic film of the internal structures of the body. In some cases, the images are captured and processed electronically. The value of these images explains why doctors and dentists conduct as many as 35 million X-ray examinations each year in the UK.

Approximate number of clinical procedures involving radiation exposure each year in the UK	
CATEGORY	NUMBER OF EXAMINATIONS
Medical X-ray examinations	25 000 000
Dental X-ray examinations	10 000 000
Nuclear medicine procedures	500 000
Radiotherapy treatments	150 000

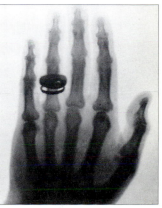

First X-ray of a hand (Frau Röntgen)

The parts of the body most frequently examined are the chest, limbs, and teeth, each accounting for about 25% of the total number of examinations. Doses are fairly low – about 0.02 mSv from a chest examination, for example. Effective doses from other types of examination, such as the lower spine, are higher because organs and tissues that are more sensitive to radiation are exposed to a greater degree. Examinations of the lower bowel using a barium enema result in a substantial dose around 7 mSv; only 1% or so of all examinations are of this type.

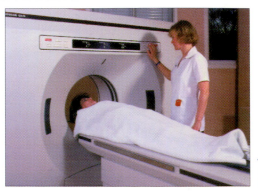

A patient undergoes CT scan

7

Medical uses of ionising radiation

....

Nuclear medicine

Typical doses to patients from conventional X-ray and computed tomography examinations in the UK

	Dose (mSv)	
Examination	Conventional X-ray	Computed Tomography
Head	0.03	2
Teeth	<0.1	–
Chest	0.02	8
Abdomen	0.7	10
Pelvis	0.7	10
Lower spine	0.7	6
Lower bowel	7	–
Limbs and joints	<0.01	–

Computed tomography (CT) has increased considerably in recent years to the point where approximately 4% of all procedures in diagnostic radiology are CT scans. With this technique, a fan-shaped beam of X-rays is rotated around the patient and registered on the opposite side by a row of detectors. An image of a slice or section through the patient is then reconstructed by a computer and conveys superior diagnostic information. However, doses in CT can be an order of magnitude higher than those from conventional X-ray examinations.

Diagnostic radiology as a whole makes a contribution of about 20 000 man Sv to the annual collective dose from ionising radiation in the UK. Of this, CT contributes about 40%, examinations of the lower bowel about 10%, and chest examinations about 1%. It is clear from these figures that some relatively infrequent procedures give a far greater dose to the population than the more common examinations. Further, they explain why it is important that a CT scan should not be used if an ordinary X-ray examination would suffice for a sound diagnosis.

Nuclear medicine

For a diagnostic procedure in nuclear medicine, the patient is given a radionuclide in a carrying substance, such as a pharmaceutical, which is preferentially taken up by the tissue or organ under study; administration may be by injection, ingestion or inhalation. The radionuclide emits gamma rays.

Most of the diagnostic procedures make use of the radionuclide technetium-99m: it has a half-life of 6 hours, gives off gamma rays with an energy of 0.14 MeV, can be conveniently prepared in the hospital, and readily labels a variety of carrying substances. A special detector called a gamma camera is used to observe how the organs or tissue behave or how quickly the radionuclide moves.

Individual doses from technetium scans are comparable to those in diagnostic radiology. The collective dose from nuclear medicine is, however, an order of magnitude less.

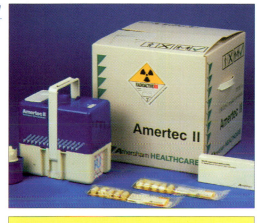

Typical doses to patients from common investigations of organs in nuclear medicine	
ORGAN SCAN	EFFECTIVE DOSE (mSv)
Brain	7
Bone	4
Thyroid, lung	1
Liver, kidney	1

When radionuclides are used for treatment rather than diagnosis, much greater activities are given to the patient and much higher doses are given to the target tissues or organs. The treatment of an overactive thyroid gland – hyperthyroidism – is probably the most common therapeutic procedure, the radionuclide being iodine-131. This illustrates a paradox in radiological protection: the beneficial use of a radioactive substance which in other circumstances becomes an environmental contaminant.

Family and friends of a patient to whom a radionuclide has been given may sometimes be advised by the hospital to take appropriate precautions against inadvertent exposure to themselves from the residual activity.

Radiotherapy

This technique is used to cure cancers or at least to alleviate the most distressing symptoms. A beam of high energy X-rays, gamma rays or electrons is directed towards the diseased tissue so as to give it a high dose while sparing the surrounding healthy tissue. If a tumour is deep in the body, the beam is pointed at it from several directions so as to reduce the incidental damage. Another form of treatment, in which a radiation source is placed in or on the body for a short period, is used for particular forms of cancer: it is called *brachytherapy*.

Tumours require absorbed doses of tens of gray to kill the cancer cells effectively. Considerable care is required to deliver accurate doses: too low or too high doses may lead to incomplete treatment or unacceptable side-effects. As radiotherapy doses are strong, such treatment is only used when the outlook for a cure or relief is good and when other methods of treatment would be less effective.

Although radiotherapy can cure the original cancer, it may possibly cause cancer in other tissues or adverse genetic effects in subsequent children. Most people who receive radiotherapy are, however, past the age to have children and too old for delayed cancers to occur. So the aim of radiotherapy is to maximise the effectiveness of treatment while minimising the adverse side-effects.

Reference doses

Since diagnostic radiology is so widely used and the collective dose so large, it is important to avoid unnecessary exposures and keep the essential exposures as low as possible. The decision whether to prescribe an X-ray examination is a matter of medical judgement made in the best interests of the patient.

When decided upon, the dose to the patient should be the lowest possible compatible with accurate diagnosis. Physicians take particular care to minimise doses in paediatric examinations.

Methods of minimising doses include the use of good equipment that is well maintained, properly adjusted and skilfully operated, and having a programme of quality assurance in the X-ray department. Doses from the same X-ray examination may vary from patient to patient because of differences in size and shape, but they should generally fall below an agreed value. This, as we mentioned in Chapter 5, is called a reference dose. A set of reference doses for the more common X-ray examinations has been recommended in the UK. Adherence to them is causing a downward trend in doses throughout the country.

Total doses

If we consider diagnostic procedures in radiology and nuclear medicine, the collective dose in the UK is about 22 000 man Sv in a year, which implies 0.37 mSv each when averaged across the entire population. The reality is, however, that young people do not have many X-rays and that the likelihood of needing an examination increases with age; this implies a lower probability, in general, of any consequential cancers being expressed.

7

Medical uses of ionising radiation

Total doses

8 Occupational exposure to ionising radiation

Exposure to ionising radiation occurs in many occupations, most obviously to those who work in the nuclear power industry. Artificial sources of radiation are also commonly used in the manufacturing and service industries, in areas of defence, in research institutions, and in universities. Moreover, we have seen in Chapter 7 that they are extensively used by health professionals.

Common uses of radiation in industry

Radiography of welds and joints

Security inspection of bags and parcels

Level gauging of container contents

Sterilisation of some medical supplies

Static elimination in paper production

Analysis of specimens for quality control

n industrial thickness gauge

Some workers are also exposed to natural sources of radiation in such circumstances that a measure of supervision and protection is required. This is particularly true of exposure to radon in mines and in ordinary premises throughout the areas of the country worst affected by radon. It is also true of aircrew who are exposed to elevated levels of cosmic rays at flying altitudes.

Many people who work with radiation wear personal monitoring devices such as a small photographic film or some thermo-luminescent (TL) material in a special holder. These register the radiation incident on the body from external sources and yield an estimate of the dose. NRPB issues about half a million such devices each year as a monitoring service.

For airborne activity in the workplace, whether of artificial or natural origin, it is usually best to sample the air that the worker breathes, measure it, and then estimate the internal dose. In some cases, it may be possible to measure activity in excreta and infer the dose or indeed measure the activity in the body directly with sensitive detectors.

8 Occupational exposure to ionising radiation

Artificial sources

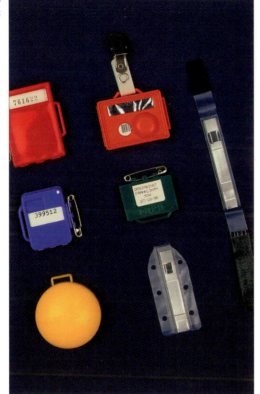

The objective always is to get the best possible estimate of dose for comparison with limits.

All told, about a quarter of a million people are occupationally exposed to ionising radiation in the UK, but the collective dose is about 380 man Sv in a year. More workers are exposed to artificial than natural sources; individual doses from the latter are, however, an order of magnitude greater. The average dose overall in occupational exposure is around 1.5 mSv in a year.

Scale of occupational exposure and indicative doses in the UK		
TYPE OF EXPOSURE	NUMBER OF WORKERS	ANNUAL DOSES (mSv)
Artificial radiation	150 000	0.33
Natural radiation	100 000	3.30

Artificial sources

Occupational exposure to artificial sources of radiation occurs predominantly in the nuclear and general industries and the health professions. Doses have declined steeply in the last decade or so for reasons that we have explained in Chapter 5; this remark applies to average as well as individual doses.

Annual effective doses in the UK from occupational exposure to radiation	
SOURCE	DOSE (mSv)
Artificial sources	
Nuclear industry	0.7
Defence work	0.8
General industry	0.4
Research and education	0.1
Health professions	0.1
Radon sources	
Coal mines	0.6
Metal mines	4.5
Work premises	5.0
Cosmic sources	
Civil air transport	2.0

Average doses from all types of occupational exposure, including the nuclear industry, are now below 1 mSv in a year. Some tens of workers may receive more than 15 mSv in a year, particularly industrial radiographers; few if any receive more than 20 mSv in a year except under unsatisfactory conditions that may attract warning or prosecution by the regulatory authorities.

Doses in the health professions – medical, dental and veterinary – are generally very low, but there are still matters of concern. Some clinical procedures with diagnostic radiology require the physician to be close to the patient and at risk of appreciable exposure. X-ray equipment and procedures in veterinary practices are sometimes inadequate.

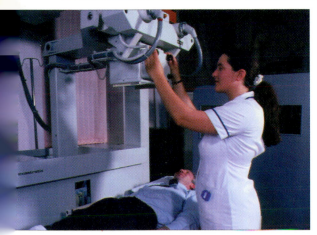

Medical iography

Natural sources

Occupational exposure to natural sources of radiation occurs mainly in coal mines, buildings, and airplanes. Relatively few people work in mines other than coal and in the processing of ores with levels of natural activity appreciably above average: the doses incurred are nevertheless monitored routinely.

Radon levels – and doses – are low in coal mines because the ventilation is usually good: few if any miners exceed 15 mSv in a year. The state of ventilation in metal and other mines is not always as satisfactory, so the average dose is much higher and a fraction of the workforce does exceed this dose.

About half of the people occupationally exposed to natural radiation work in shops, offices, schools and other premises in radon-prone areas of the country. Within these well-defined areas, the average dose is appreciable. Five per cent or so of the workers receive more than 15 mSv in a year and a smaller percentage 20 mSv or more. Radon levels vary markedly from day to day because of the way buildings are heated and ventilated, so short measurements of radon in air may be misleading. The best remedy for high radon levels is the same as in houses – reduced air pressure under the floor.

8
***Occupational
exposure to
ionising
radiation***

*Natural
sources*

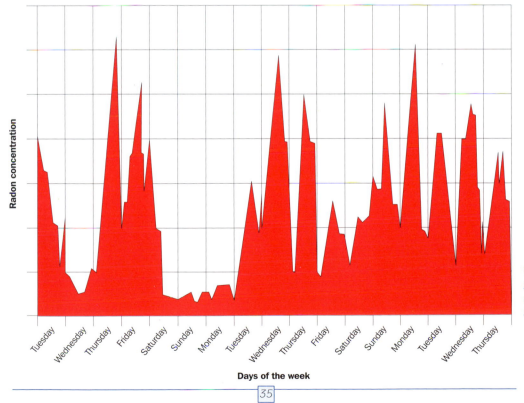

*Variations
in radon
concentration
in a building*

*Typical
doses on
air flights
from London*

Flight No.	Destination	Flight Time (h)	Dose (mSv)
NR14	Paris	1	0.004
RP15	Madrid	2	0.010
NR23	Rome	3	0.014
RP18	Kiev	4	0.018
PB71	New York	7	0.042
PB77	Los Angeles	13	0.069
PB93	Tokyo	14	0.078

For comparison, 24 hours on the ground would result in a dose of 0.002 mSv from cosmic and terrestrial sources.

**8
Occupational
exposure to
ionising
radiation**

Total doses

Doses to aircrews from cosmic rays depend on the routes flown and the time airborne. On average, the annual dose is around 2 mSv, but it could be twice as much for long flights continually at high altitudes. By the nature of the radiation and the operations, such doses are unavoidable. A pregnant member of an aircrew will have a schedule of work to avoid a dose above 1 mSv to the unborn child.

Total doses

As indicated here, the collective effective dose from occupational exposure to ionising radiation is about 380 man Sv in a year in the UK. Spread over the entire population, this implies an annual dose approaching 0.007 mSv, a relatively minor contribution to the overall value of 2.6 mSv.

9 Environmental pollution

We have seen in Chapter 6 that natural radionuclides pervade our environment. This chapter is about the artificial radionuclides that have been widely dispersed by events such as tests of nuclear weapons in the atmosphere and the Chernobyl accident and by the deliberate discharge of radioactive wastes from nuclear and other installations. Such radionuclides find their way from air and water on to the ground and into foodstuffs and so deliver radiation doses in various ways to human beings.

Weapons tests

When nuclear weapons are tested above ground, they inject a variety of radionuclides from hydrogen-3 (tritium) to plutonium-241 into the upper atmosphere. From there, they transfer slowly to the lower atmosphere and then to earth. Around 500 atmospheric explosions were conducted before the limited test ban treaty in 1963 with a few more until 1980. By now, however, the concentrations of radionuclides in air, rain and human diet are much lower than the peak values in the early 1960s.

Currently the most important radionuclides in terms of human exposure are carbon-14, strontium-90 and caesium-137: minute quantities are ingested with food and drink. Residual activity in the ground of radionuclides that emit gamma rays also causes a slight degree of human exposure. Internal and external irradiation contribute about equally to the average effective dose of 0.004 mSv in a year in the UK: this compares with a peak of 0.014 mSv in 1963. The collective dose is now about 240 man Sv in a year.

Pathways of exposure in the environment

Rain washing radioactive materials out of the air

External radiation direct from cloud

Internal dose from radioactive materials in the air

External dose direct from radioactive materials deposited on the ground

Internal dose from eating and drinking radioactive materials in food

Internal dose from breathing in sea spray and sand

Chernobyl accident

An explosion in a nuclear reactor at the Chernobyl nuclear power plant on 26 April 1986 caused the release of substantial quantities of radionuclides during a period of ten days. Airborne material was dispersed throughout Europe from the site in the Ukraine and reached the UK within a week. As the contaminated air spread over the UK, local weather conditions largely determined where the radionuclides were to fall: heavy rain in the northwest caused more to be deposited there.

In terms of dose to people, the most significant radionuclides were iodine-131, caesium-134 and caesium-137. Almost all of the dose was caused by external irradiation from radionuclides on the ground and by internal irradiation from radionuclides in foodstuffs. In the first year after the accident, the average dose from Chernobyl contaminants was about 0.02 mSv. It has now declined to 0.001 mSv in a year for the country as a whole, implying a collective dose approaching 60 man Sv annually.

Annual doses in the UK at present from weapons fallout and Chernobyl contaminants		
SOURCE	AVERAGE DOSE (mSv)	COLLECTIVE DOSE (man Sv)
Weapons fallout	0.004	230
Chernobyl contaminants	0.001	60

For the wetter upland regions of the UK, however, the greater deposition of activity from weapons testing and the Chernobyl accident causes annual doses of about 0.012 mSv.

Radioactive discharges

Artificial radionuclides are discharged to the environment by the nuclear power industry, defence establishments, research organisations, hospitals and general industry. Discharges of any significance are subject to statutory control: they must be authorised and monitored. Owners or operators of the facilities from which radionuclides are discharged carry out monitoring programmes as do the regulatory agencies.

The nuclear power industry discharges by far the most activity. At each stage of the *nuclear fuel cycle*, a variety of radionuclides are released in the form of liquids, gases or solid particles. The nature of the effluent depends on the particular operation or process.

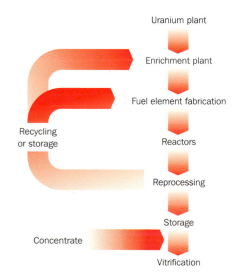

Uranium plant

Enrichment plant

Fuel element fabrication

Reactors

Reprocessing

Storage

Vitrification

Recycling or storage

Concentrate

During fuel preparation, when the uranium is enriched and the fuel elements are fabricated, discharges mainly contain uranium and thorium with the associated decay products – these being natural of course. Annual doses to the most exposed group of people near the facilities are about 0.14 mSv, most of which is due to discharges elsewhere in the fuel cycle. The collective dose to the whole population of the UK is less than 0.1 man Sv annually.

In reactor operation, airborne discharges to the atmosphere give rise to an annual collective dose of 5 man Sv or so, principally from hydrogen-3, carbon-14 and sulphur-35 with the annual dose to those most exposed being 0.082 mSv. The collective dose from liquid discharges to coastal waters, arising from the consumption of radionuclides in seafoods, is much smaller, but individual doses locally are dominated by discharges from fuel reprocessing. Some older nuclear reactors cause direct irradiation of people near the power station: annual doses of 0.5 mSv have been estimated for them.

Discharges of radionuclides to the Irish Sea from the fuel reprocessing facilities at Sellafield in Cumbria have been greatly reduced in the past decade or so. The annual dose to the most exposed people – those who eat local seafood – is some 0.14 mSv, mainly from actinides in shellfish. Discharges to air of strontium-90 and other radionuclides lead to individual doses that are less than 0.055 mSv annually from the consumption of local milk and vegetables. The collective dose from airborne discharges, mainly due to carbon-14 in foodstuffs, is approximately 1 man Sv annually. From liquid discharges, it is about 4 man Sv annually, mainly due to caesium-137 in fish.

Total doses

None of the other facilities that discharge artificial radionuclides to the environment causes doses much above 0.02 mSv in a year to the most exposed people; nor do they make a significant contribution to collective dose. In round terms, therefore, the maximum effective dose from the discharge of artificial radionuclides is about 0.14 mSv in a year and the collective effective dose about 10 man Sv in a year or 0.0002 mSv when averaged throughout the entire population.

Total doses

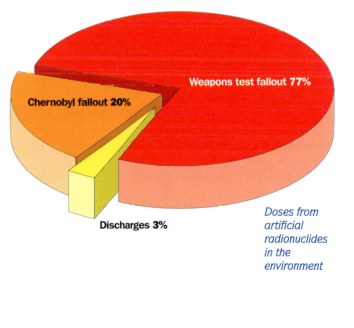

Doses from artificial radionuclides in the environment

Annual doses due to discharges from the nuclear fuel cycle in the UK			
STAGE OF CYCLE	TYPE OF EFFLUENT	MOST EXPOSED PEOPLE (mSv)	COLLECTIVE DOSE (man Sv)
Fuel fabrication	Airborne	<0.014	<0.1
	Liquid	0.14	<0.01
Reactor operation	Airborne	0.045	5
	Liquid	0.082	<0.2
Fuel reprocessing	Airborne	<0.055	1
	Liquid	0.14	4

10 Nuclear power

Nuclear reactors have been producing electricity since the 1950s, and the electricity supply industry now operates power reactors at twelve sites in the UK. Some of these contain two stations; together they produce about 20% of the electric power generated in the UK. The newest reactor is at Sizewell: a number of older stations have stopped operating.

Nuclear reactors

Nuclear reactors depend for their operation on a reaction between neutrons and the atomic nuclei of the fuel. Uranium, the fuel for reactors in the UK, consists principally of two isotopes, uranium-235 and uranium-238. In natural uranium, the fuel for early reactors, those isotopes are in the proportion of 0.7% and 99.3%, respectively, by weight. The *enriched uranium* for later reactors contains about 2.5% of uranium-235.

Energy is released when a uranium-235 nucleus absorbs a neutron and undergoes *fission*, that is, it splits into two large energetic fragments or *fission products*, accompanied by the release of several high energy or *fast neutrons* and some gamma radiation. The neutrons are slowed in the reactor so that they induce further fissions in the uranium-235: such neutrons are often called *thermal neutrons* and the reactors that rely upon them *thermal reactors*. By contrast, when a nucleus of uranium-238 absorbs a fast neutron it becomes uranium-239, which decays to form plutonium-239. This will also fission and capture neutrons to form isotopes of additional actinides such as americium or curium.

Power station sites
- 🔴 Operating
- ⭕ Closed

Other nuclear sites
- 🟦 Operating

Dounreay
Torness
Hunterston
Chapelcross
Sellafield
Hartlepool
Calder Hall
Heysham
Springfields
Wylfa
Capenhurst
Trawsfynydd
Harwell
Sizewell
Berkeley
Bradwell
Oldbury
Hinkley Point
Aldermaston
Dungeness
Winfrith

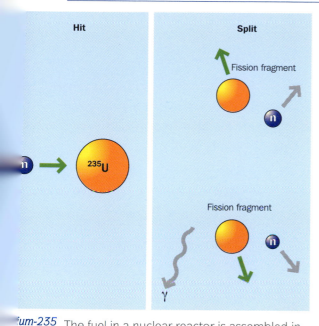

Hit

Split

Fission fragment

^{235}U

Fission fragment

γ

Uranium-235 fission

A coolant, usually water or gas, conducts heat away from the fuel and then passes through heat exchangers to make steam. The steam then drives turbine generators to make electricity.

The main types of reactor designed in the UK use graphite as a moderator and pressurised carbon dioxide gas as the coolant: the early types are called *Magnox reactors* and the later types *Advanced Gas Cooled Reactors (AGR)*. Most other countries use *Pressurised Water Reactors (PWR)* where water acts both as moderator and as coolant: the newest reactor at Sizewell is a PWR.

The fuel is sealed in metal containers, and the core is contained in a pressure vessel. Massive concrete shielding helps to absorb the intense radiation emitted by the core during and after operation. A building further contains the reactors and usually the heat exchangers.

The fuel in a nuclear reactor is assembled in an array called the core which also contains the *moderator*, a material, generally water or graphite, that slows or thermalises the neutrons.

10
Nuclear
power

Nuclear reactors

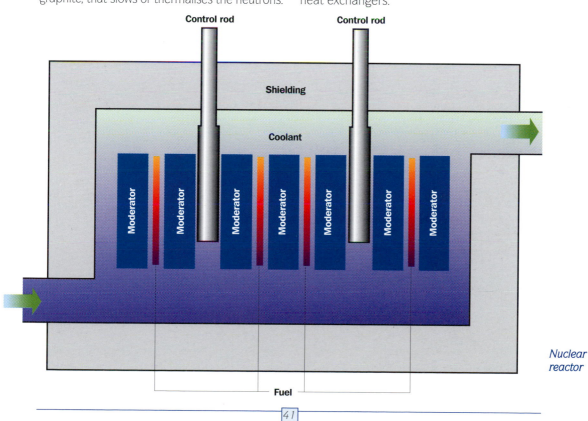

Control rod   **Control rod**

Shielding

Coolant

Moderator   Moderator   Moderator   Moderator   Moderator   Moderator   Moderator

Fuel

Nuclear reactor

Fresh fuel is only mildly radioactive and can be handled without shielding. Once in the reactor, however, there is an enormous increase of activity due mainly to the fission products in the fuel; this means that an accident at the reactor could release significant activity. After removal from the reactor, the spent fuel remains hot and must be cooled as well as shielded to reduce melting and prevent human exposure.

Waste management

In Chapter 9 we described the discharge of effluents from the nuclear fuel cycle, but there are also other radioactive wastes. They fall into three broad categories according to activity: low level, intermediate level, and high level.

Low level wastes consist of items such as paper, clothing, and laboratory equipment that have been used in areas where radioactive substances are handled, as well as contaminated soil and building materials. Intermediate level wastes include ion exchange materials that are used in the treatment of gaseous and liquid effluents before they are discharged

to the environment, the sludges that accumulate in the cooling ponds where spent fuel is stored, and materials contaminated with plutonium. In the UK, high level waste refers only to the highly active liquid produced when spent fuel is reprocessed. In countries not committed to reprocessing, spent fuel itself is regarded as high level waste.

The aims of *waste management* are to process the wastes in such a way as to make them suitable for storage and disposal and to dispose of them so that there are no unacceptable risks to present and future generations. Here *disposal* implies simply that there is no intention to retrieve them rather than that it would be impossible to do so.

Low level wastes do not generally need processing: they can be packaged, sometimes after compaction, and disposed of directly to an authorised burial site. Most waste in this category from the nuclear fuel cycle is disposed of in shallow burial facilities at a site near Sellafield in Cumbria.

Most intermediate level wastes do not occur in a form suitable for direct disposal; they have to be mixed into an inert material such as concrete, bitumen or resin. In the past, some of these wastes were dumped at sea, but since that has been embargoed, all are stored at the various nuclear sites around the country awaiting decision on the method of disposal. Among the options is a repository deep underground in good geological conditions.

As in other countries, all the high level waste produced in the UK is stored in one form or another. Liquid waste from reprocessing operations is kept in special cooled tanks at Sellafield. Facilities to solidify it by incorporation in vitreous material also exist at Sellafield. The glass blocks will be stored for several

Waste categories

LOW LEVEL WASTES
Contain various radionuclides in general refuse and rubble.
Low activity, high bulk

INTERMEDIATE LEVEL WASTES
Contain larger quantities of fission products and actinides with long half-lives.
Low heat creation, high bulk

HIGH LEVEL WASTES
Contain most of the fission poducts and actinides from the fuel cycle.
High heat creation, low bulk

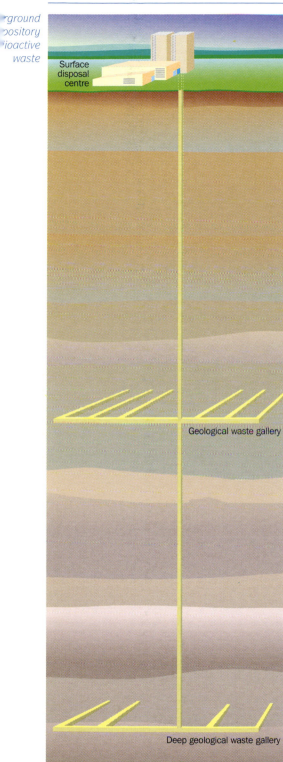

Surface
disposal
centre

Geological waste gallery

Deep geological waste gallery

decades to allow them
to cool before eventual
disposal, probably
underground.

Decommissioning

There has been no
complete *decommissioning*
of major nuclear facilities so
far in the UK, although
practical experience has
been gained on the
prototype advanced gas
cooled reactor at Sellafield.
The closure of some
Magnox reactors and the
fact that others are
approaching the end of
useful life have, however,
focused attention on the problems
associated with the process.

Decommissioning of the more radioactive
parts of a reactor will require strict control of
operations to avoid excessive radiation doses
to workers; complicated techniques of remote
handling will be essential. Large volumes of
low and intermediate level radioactive waste
will arise, and a management strategy to
optimise the protection of workers and the
public will need to be devised.

Disposal criteria

There has been considerable discussion of
the criteria to be used in judging the
acceptability of waste disposal methods both
from a radiological protection point of view
and from the wider social perspective.
The consensus would seem to be that people
in future generations should be protected to
the same degree as they would be at
present. However, it is difficult to translate
this requirement into practical standards of
radiological protection: for example, activity

*Vitrified
high level
radioactive
waste*

Steel
casing

Vitrified
waste

*10
**Nuclear
power***

*Disposal
criteria*

may only emerge from a deep repository many thousands of years later, and we have no idea what the habits or ways of life of our descendants will be so far into the future.

NRPB advice on radiological protection criteria for the disposal of solid radioactive waste is intended to limit future risks to acceptable levels. It recommends that the risk of a serious health effect among the most exposed groups of people from a single disposal site should not exceed 1 in 100 000 annually. NRPB recognises the uncertainties in the risk calculations and furthermore that calculations extending a million years or more into the future are scientifically uncertain. For disposal to land of low and intermediate level wastes, the regulatory authorities have set a target for a single repository: the annual risk of death for the people at greatest risk at any time should be no more than 1 in 1 000 000.

A second requirement is to apply the principle that all exposures should be as low as reasonably achievable once economic and social factors have been taken into account. This means that the various options for managing a particular type of waste – including treatment, immobilisation, packaging and disposal – should be compared on the basis of the associated risks, costs, and other less quantifiable but no less important factors. Some of this comparison will be within the scope of radiological protection, but other influences could determine the eventual decision.

The difficult question for society about waste disposal is what weight to give now to a mathematical probability of harmful effects in the distant future. This problem is not peculiar to waste disposal nor to radiological protection, although it is particularly pointed here. The most ethical answer would be to assume that present conditions persist and that harm to future generations is of equal importance as harm to this generation. This response must of course be tempered by the uncertainties of making predictions of potential effects centuries and millennia from now.

10
Nuclear
power

Disposal criteria

11 Nuclear emergencies

An emergency may arise at a nuclear installation and lead to the accidental release of radioactive material, its dispersion beyond the boundary of the site, and the need for urgent measures to protect the public. In some circumstances, the release may be brief, in others prolonged. Although such accidents may be rare, it is prudent to be prepared for them.

This chapter is mainly about emergency plans for nuclear accidents at major installations such as reactor stations and the provisions in the UK for protecting the public. The same approach more or less applies to serious accidents in any other circumstance, such as transport or military operations, that could result in the release of radionuclides.

To ensure that there is adequate protection against accidents, the Health and Safety Executive as licensing authority requires a detailed safety analysis of major nuclear installations such as reactors. This analysis identifies potential accident sequences that might lead to the release of radionuclides. The sequence leading to the largest release that can reasonably be foreseen is called a *reference accident*. Emergency plans are based on it, but they could be strengthened and extended in the unlikely event of a more severe accident.

Should an accident occur at a reactor, for example, various radionuclides in gaseous, volatile, or particulate form could be expelled to the atmosphere. They would then be borne away in a plume by the wind and be dispersed and diluted. Some would fall to the ground, particularly if it were raining. The concentration of radionuclides in the air

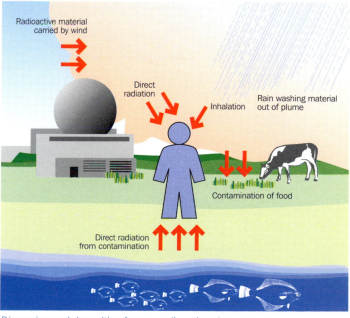

Radioactive material carried by wind

Direct radiation

Inhalation

Rain washing material out of plume

Contamination of food

Direct radiation from contamination

Dispersion and deposition from a radioactive plume

would decrease rapidly downwind from the site as would the attendant hazard: even so, appreciable activity could be deposited on the ground at considerable distances.

Countermeasures

It may be necessary to take action to reduce the radiation dose to the people living nearby. Various countermeasures could be undertaken singly or in combination.

People may be advised to stay indoors or even leave home until the plume has blown over or the release has been stopped. People could take non-radioactive iodine tablets to prevent radioactive iodine reaching the thyroid gland. It may also be necessary to introduce temporary restrictions on the distribution of milk and vegetables and other foods produced locally. Some easy countermeasures might be taken such as hosing roads and paths or cutting and removing grass from gardens so as to remove surface activity.

Countermeasures in an emergency
Sheltering indoors from the plume
Temporary evacuation of homes
Administration of iodine tablets
Ban on contaminated foodstuffs

When the emergency has passed, it may be necessary to introduce other countermeasures during a prolonged recovery period so as to protect the public from the residual activity.

Emergency arrangements

There are elaborate and well-rehearsed plans for dealing with nuclear emergencies in the UK and for those that might occur overseas and affect the UK.

Every nuclear site in the UK must by law have an emergency plan and let the local people know about it. The plan will involve the operator's staff, the local authority, and the emergency services. Government departments and agencies and NRPB will also become involved: each will deploy its radiological resources and expertise.

Government organisations in emergency arrangements
Department of Trade and Industry
Scottish Office
Ministry of Agriculture, Fisheries and Food
Department of the Environment, Transport and the Regions
Ministry of Defence
Welsh Office
Northern Ireland Office
Department of Health
Health and Safety Executive
National Radiological Protection Board
Environment Agency
Scottish Environment Protection Agency

In the early stages of an accident, the operator will advise the police on measures to protect the public. Soon a coordinating centre away from the site will be set up at which all the participants, with a government technical adviser, will agree actions to protect the public: these will include environmental monitoring as well as appropriate countermeasures. Arrangements will be made to brief the news media.

The national response to a nuclear emergency will be coordinated by the Department of Trade and Industry in London or by the Scottish Office in Edinburgh for accidents in Scotland. Several government departments and agencies will participate in the preparation of briefings for ministers and parliament. The Department of Trade and Industry is also responsible for notifying overseas governments and international organisations.

The frequency and scale of exercises to test the emergency arrangements are determined by the Health and Safety Executive.

Accidents occurring overseas should in general have less radiological significance than accidents in the UK simply because of the greater distances for the contaminants to travel. However, the Chernobyl disaster showed that there could be consequences far away and led to development of a response plan under the aegis of the Department of the Environment, Transport and the Regions.

This plan includes an international notification scheme to which the UK subscribes and a national detection scheme known as the Radioactive Incident Monitoring Network. RIMNET has an array of automatic instruments around the country to detect increases in gamma dose rates. This system would also be an important source of information after an accident in the UK.

RIMNET monitoring station

Intervention standards

Taking countermeasures after accidents is another example of the procedure that ICRP calls intervention. We have seen in Chapter 5 that intervention must be justified and optimised. It is only necessary to add that countermeasures must be taken to avoid doses high enough to cause obvious injury in anyone exposed – but especially children.

NRPB has recommended *Emergency Reference Levels (ERL)* of dose for the introduction of countermeasures to protect the public: these are used to identify which actions would be most suitable in particular circumstances. For each countermeasure, there is a lower and upper level of dose. Below the first, the countermeasure is unlikely to be worthwhile: above the second, it would be worthwhile in most circumstances.

11

Nuclear emergencies

Intervention standards

Emergency reference levels for countermeasures		Dose level (mSv)	
Countermeasure	Organ	Lower	Upper
Sheltering	Whole body	3	30
Evacuation	Whole body	30	300
Iodine administration	Thyroid	30	300

One outcome of the Chernobyl accident was the introduction by the European Commission of regulations on the radioactive contamination of food; they apply in all member states.

Intervention levels for some foods and for water in the event of a future nuclear accident (Bq kg^{-1})				
	European Commission		NRPB	
Important radionuclides	Baby foods	Milk and cream	Most foods	Drinking water
Strontium-90	75	125	750	125
Iodine-131	150	500	2000	500
Plutonium-239	1	20	80	20
Caesium-137	400	1000	1250	1000

These European interventions levels are rather stringent in terms of the dose that might be averted by introducing them. NRPB extended the approach to drinking water but noted that a general relaxation of all the levels by an order of magnitude could be justified.

Minor incidents

Discrete quantities of radioactive material and radiation sources are widely used in general industry, research organisations, and hospitals and they are routinely transported between locations, so incidents and mishaps, such as damage or loss, occasionally occur. In the absence or failure of appropriate contingency plans, police forces are able to activate the National Arrangements for Incidents involving Radioactivity. Coordinated by NRPB, NAIR draws on the services of experts at institutions around the country – principally large hospitals – to provide assistance for radiological protection.

11

Nuclear emergencies

Minor incidents

12 Electromagnetic fields and radiation

We are all exposed to *electromagnetic fields* from a variety of sources that use electrical energy. These fields exist as *electromagnetic waves* with a wide range of *wavelengths* and *frequencies*. They occupy the region of the *electromagnetic spectrum* that ends in virtually static fields and is bordered by optical radiations. The reason we call them electromagnetic fields rather than *electromagnetic radiations* is because of our separate interest in the electric and magnetic components, particularly at extremely low frequencies.

Wavelength and frequency are inversely related to each other, so the lower the frequency the longer the wavelength and vice versa. This chapter is about electromagnetic fields *(EMF)* with frequencies less than 300 GHz where the wavelength in air is 1 mm. It includes, for example, the electricity mains frequency of 50 Hz with a wavelength of 6000 km. When the strength of a field changes with time, as for alternating current supplies of electricity, it is said to be time varying.

*Electromagnetic
fields and
radiation*

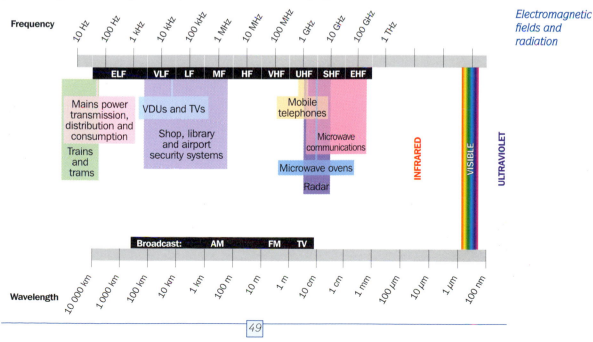

Non-ionising radiation is the term generally applied to fields in this region of the electromagnetic spectrum and to radiations in the neighbouring optical region. In contrast to ionising radiation, exposure to artificial electromagnetic fields from some parts of the spectrum, such as power and broadcasting frequencies, is much greater than that from natural fields.

Common sources

The most common sources of exposure to time-varying electromagnetic fields are electrical power lines, electrical appliances at home and work, and various radio, television, and radiotelephone transmitters. There is a common low level of exposure to *radio-frequency radiation* everywhere that radio or television signals are received. The general public may also be exposed to low level fields from microwave communications links, radar systems, and common products such as television and computer displays. Higher exposures can arise momentarily close to mobile telephones and other portable radio antennas.

The degree of exposure to these fields depends on the strength of the source and the distance from it. Field strength decreases rapidly with distance. In the case of directional sources such as microwave dishes, strength also decreases rapidly out of the main beam. High power broadcast systems and highly directional radar systems do not generally give significant exposure to electromagnetic fields except for maintenance workers or engineers. Millions of people, however, come close to electrical appliances where the associated electromagnetic fields cause uneven and partial exposure of the body. These fields may be characterised by *electric field strength* and *magnetic flux density*.

During recent decades, the use of electrical energy has increased substantially to supply power at mains frequency and for broadcasting and telecommunications. At the radiofrequencies used in broadcasting, human exposure will have increased in proportion with power; at telecommunications frequencies, the proliferation of mobile telephones will have increased the exposure of those who use them. The greater use of electrical appliances in homes will have increased exposure to 50 Hz fields but to what degree is not clear: the magnetic fields, for instance,

Electromagnetic fields from electrical cables and appliances and comparison with natural values for static fields

SOURCE	CONDITIONS	ELECTRIC FIELD STRENGTH	MAGNETIC FLUX DENSITY
High voltage power lines	400 kV, from 25 m to midline	$1-10$ kV m^{-1}	$8-40$ μT
Electrical appliances	Ambient levels Levels at 30 cm	$1-10$ V m^{-1} $10-250$ V m^{-1}	$0.01-1$ μT $0.01-30$ μT
TV sets and VDUs	Levels at 30 cm	$1-10$ V m^{-1}	up to 0.2 μT
Mobile telephones	Levels from 10 down to 2 cm	$90-270$ V m^{-1}	$0.3-1$ μT
Static natural fields	Fair weather Stormy weather	$120-150$ V m^{-1} 10 kV m^{-1}	50 μT 50 μT

depend in a complex way on domestic wiring and earthing practice and on the currents flowing in cables and wires.

Immediate effects

The interaction of electromagnetic fields with the human body and the harmful effects they may have depend on frequency.

With static electric fields – that is, fields with no time variation – we can sense the electric charge induced on the surface of the body by the way it affects the hairs on the head. For most people, this becomes annoying at electric field strengths above 25 kV m⁻¹ (kilovolts per metre). In guidelines on human exposure to electromagnetic fields, NRPB advises that this annoying sensation should be avoided.

Static magnetic fields, it would seem, do not produce any detrimental effects on people exposed for short periods at magnetic flux densities up to 2 T (tesla). Moreover, long-term exposure up to 200 mT (millitesla) should not have any adverse effects.

Electromagnetic fields at frequencies below 100 kHz or so, which include the electric mains frequency of 50 Hz, can induce electric charge on the surface of the body and electric current within the body. Electric fields from high voltage power lines, for example, can make body hairs vibrate, although most people would not notice this at field strengths below 12 kV m⁻¹ or so. In some circumstances, moreover, people can experience annoying microshocks from metal objects.

Volunteer experiments have shown that exposure to intense, low frequency magnetic fields can induce electric currents throughout the human body which stimulate nerves. Exposure to much less intense time-varying fields can cause faint, flickering sensations – magnetic phosphenes – due to electrical effects on the cells in the retina. NRPB guidance on exposure to electromagnetic fields is intended to avoid such effects; it therefore recommends that no *current density* greater than 10 mA m⁻² (milliamperes per square metre) should be induced in tissues of the central nervous system. This is about ten times the typical current density generated by normal nerve activity.

Adverse effects of electromagnetic fields with guideline values recommended by NRPB for the restriction of human exposure			
FIELD	EFFECT	QUANTITY	VALUE
Static electric fields	Electric charge on body surface	Electric field strength	25 kV m⁻¹
Static magnetic fields	Vertigo, nausea	Magnetic flux density Average throughout 24 h	2 T 200 mT
Frequencies less than 100 kHz	Electric charge on body surface Disturbance of nerves and muscles	Electric field strength Induced current density	12 kV m⁻¹ 10 mA m⁻²
Frequencies from 100 kHz to 10 GHz	Increased body temperature	Specific energy absorption rate	0.4 W kg⁻¹
Frequencies from 10 GHz to 300 GHz	Heating of the body surface	Incident power density	100 W m⁻²

**12
Electromagnetic
fields and
radiation**

....

*Common
sources*

Electric field

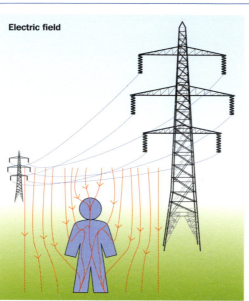

Magnetic field

At frequencies higher than 100 kHz, the major biological effect is heating. Radiofrequency *(RF)* burns are also possible at frequencies below the microwave region of the electromagnetic spectrum, that is, below 300 MHz: they are caused by the flow of current to the body through a small area of contact, such as a fingertip, from a badly earthed conducting object in a radiofrequency field.

When the conditions of exposure are such that the dominant effect on the whole body is heating from induced radiofrequency currents, the increase in temperature is much more likely to occur in narrow parts of the body such as the wrists or ankles. At microwave frequencies, heating results mainly from the alignment and relaxation of electrically polarised molecules – mostly water – in the body. Body tissues with a high water content, such as muscle, absorb power more readily than tissue with a low water content: in technical terms, they have a greater *specific energy absorption rate* or *SAR*.

The guidelines from NRPB on restricting exposure are intended to prevent radiofrequency burns and adverse effects from heating either of localised tissues or of the whole human body. Prolonged rises in body temperature of 1 C or more can cause effects such as heat exhaustion or reduced mental performance. They can be avoided, however, by restricting the whole-body SAR in a radiofrequency or microwave field to 0.4 W kg^{-1} (watts per kilogram). For comparison, metabolic processes during rest and normal muscular activity produce about 1 to 10 W kg^{-1}. In addition, restrictions on localised SAR can prevent adverse effects on temperature-sensitive tissues and organs such as the lens of the eye and the developing embryo or fetus as well as on the less sensitive tissues of the trunk and limbs.

Between frequencies of 10 and 300 GHz, which have poor penetration into the body, heating is largely confined to the surface of the body. The restriction recommended by NRPB is expressed in terms of the *power density* incident on the body, its value being 100 W m^{-2} (watts per square metre).

Most people can sense pulsed radiation of sufficient intensity between 200 MHz and 6 GHz as a buzzing or clicking noise in the head. It is thought to be caused by a small but rapid increase in temperature when the radiofrequency energy is absorbed: this generates a sound wave that stimulates the cochlea. Although there is no evidence that this effect is harmful, it can be annoying if prolonged. NRPB advises therefore that conditions of exposure in which it might occur should be avoided.

All of the NRPB guideline values given above are basic restrictions applying to occupational and public exposures without distinction but not to medical procedures. They are supported by a set of investigation levels expressed in practical, measurable quantities, compliance with which ensures that the basic restrictions are not exceeded. For time-varying electromagnetic fields, quantitative restrictions are related to average (root mean square, rms) values.

Although the immediate effects of human exposure to electromagnetic fields are well understood and restrictions are in place to avoid them, few people are exposed to such a degree that they experience the effects.

What is of more interest is the possibility of harmful effects on their health later in life from the levels of exposure in ordinary circumstances.

Delayed effects

The delayed effect that causes most concern is the possibility that electromagnetic fields might increase the risk of contracting cancer. As a result, programmes of epidemiological and biological research have been pursued by NRPB and other scientific organisations in advanced countries. NRPB also has an expert advisory group which monitors and reports on developments.

There has been a considerable number of epidemiological studies of exposure to electromagnetic fields and malignant disease. They include power frequency, radiofrequency and microwave fields; exposure of children and adults in the home; exposure of adults at work in the electricity and electronics industries. There has also been a number of extensive reviews by the NRPB advisory group, for example, and by the US National Academy of Sciences among others.

Neither the studies nor the reviews have shown clearly that electromagnetic fields give rise to cancer: in other words, causation has not been established. Some epidemiological studies do, however, suggest a weak association between exposure to power frequency fields in the home and childhood cancer; others point to a possible link between exposure at work and brain cancer in adults.

Such epidemiological studies face many difficulties. First of all, they must be based on a substantial number of malignancies and then every effort has to be made to obtain a good measure of actual exposures. It is also important to eliminate the possibility that other environmental factors may confound the outcome.

A good test of the significance of such studies is whether, singly or collectively, they establish a proportionate relationship between exposure and effect – in this case exposure and cancer. In contrast to ionising radiations (Chapter 4), electromagnetic fields have so far failed to pass this test.

Component tests for causality in epidemiological studies

Strength of association between the supposed cause and observed effect

Presence of an exposure–response relationship between them

Experimental evidence to support the postulated link

Credible biological and physical explanation of the phenomenon

There are other criteria for causation, including corroborative evidence; none is presently satisfied. It is difficult to imagine how power frequency electromagnetic fields could have any biological effect: the photon energies are many orders of magnitude below that at which ionisation occurs or chemical bonds are disrupted. What happens instead is that energy is absorbed by the movement of electric charge through and around body cells. However, this movement is likely to be so minute as to be completely masked by that which occurs naturally.

Experimental studies with animals and cells have failed to prove that electromagnetic fields can damage DNA and in so doing cause mutations in genes or chromosomes that might initiate cancer. They admit of the possibility, however – although the information is at best equivocal – that electromagnetic fields might promote the cancer process by

affecting cellular changes in a manner not yet understood. On balance there is no consistent and persuasive evidence that electromagnetic fields influence any of the accepted stages of cancer development.

It follows from the above that there is no basis on which to quantify the risk of cancer from ordinary exposure and so establish standards of protection. The subject is so important, however, that epidemiological and biological research will need to be focused on the issue of causation. Should a causal relationship be established, NRPB would not hesitate to offer advice to government on further protection of the whole community or any section of it from exposure to electro-magnetic fields.

12
Electromagnetic fields and radiation

....

Delayed effects

13 Optical radiation

Optical radiation includes the most familiar forms of radiation to which we are all exposed – ultraviolet light and radiant heat. It covers three adjacent regions of the electromagnetic spectrum, from the ultraviolet with wavelengths from 100 to 400 nm, through the visible from 400 to 770 nm, to the infrared with wavelengths from 770 nm to 1 mm. There is also merit in defining ultraviolet subregions (UVA, UVB, UVC) and infrared subregions (IRA, IRB, IRC) so as to describe biological effects.

Optical radiation does not penetrate far into human tissue, so the eyes and skin are the organs most at risk. Harmful effects may be subdivided into two main categories, photochemical and thermal. Photochemical

| **Photobiological divisions of the optical radiation spectrum with some early and late effects of overexposure** |||||
SPECTRAL DIVISION	WAVELENGTH RANGE	BIOLOGICAL EFFECTS ON THE EYE	ON THE SKIN
UVC	100 nm – 280 nm	Photokeratitis	Erythema
UVB	280 nm – 315 nm		Tanning Cancers
UVA	315 nm – 400 nm	Photochemical cataract Lens yellowing	Photoageing Cancers
Visible	400 nm – 770 nm	Retinal injury	
IRA	770 nm – 1.4 µm	Thermal cataract Retinal injury (Lenticular lesions?)	Burns
IRB	1.4 µm – 3 µm		
IRC	3 µm – 1 mm	Corneal burn	

effects are associated mainly with the ultraviolet and visible regions of the spectrum; thermal effects with the infrared and visible regions.

They may also be divided into acute and chronic categories. Among the acute injuries to the eye are photokeratitis or snowblindness (arc eye) and among the chronic injuries cataract formation. Erythema or sunburn is the most common acute injury to the skin and cancers the most serious effect of chronic exposure.

Photochemical effects result from chemical reactions in the body initiated by the absorption of photons as, for instance, in the important process of vision and the synthesis of vitamin D. Other examples include photokeratitis and erythema. For each type of reaction, there is a photon energy – the threshold – below which the effect will not occur; this translates into a threshold frequency or upper wavelength limit.

With longer wavelengths, the photons do not have enough energy to initiate the photochemical reactions; thermal effects, which lead to injury when the molecular bonds of proteins and enzymes are disrupted, become dominant in the infrared region. How much disruption and damage occurs depends on how large the temperature rise is and how long it lasts.

Although the sun is the main source of optical radiation, artificial sources are also important. They include arcs, discharge and incandescent devices, and lasers. They range from germicidal and horticultural lamps which emit radiation in the ultraviolet region, to halogen cooker hobs and heaters in the infrared region.

Ultraviolet radiation

There is more concern about protecting people against *ultraviolet radiation (UVR)* than any other region of the optical spectrum because of the steadily increasing incidence of skin cancer. NRPB has an extensive monitoring and research programme on ultraviolet radiation and an expert advisory group on the hazards to human health.

Although ultraviolet wavelengths range from 100 to 400 nm, solar ultraviolet radiation reaching the surface of the earth extends only from around 290 to 400 nm because the ultraviolet radiation at shorter wavelengths is absorbed by the atmosphere. In doing so, it interacts with oxygen to produce ozone mostly in a protective layer between altitudes of 15 and 30 km.

NRPB booklet on UVR

Sunburn in some people is followed by an increased production of melanin and increased pigmentation. A suntan offers only minimal protection against further exposure to ultraviolet radiation and is *not* an indication

Some artificial sources of optical radiation	
SPECTRAL REGION	SOURCES
Ultraviolet	Germicidal lamps, mercury discharge lamps, welding arcs, fluorescent lamps, tungsten halogen lamps, sunbeds, lasers
Visible	Fluorescent lamps, welding arcs, tungsten halogen lamps, lasers
Infrared	Welding arcs, tungsten halogen lamps, furnaces, lasers

of good health. Apart from circumstances in which a sunburn is severe, erythema is not itself a serious injury. Each exposure, no matter how slight, increases the risk of a serious effect – skin cancer.

There is clear evidence that ultraviolet radiation, and in particular UVB, can cause skin cancers of the non-melanoma type. For most people, the sun is the main source of exposure and of risk, but there is also some risk to those who are intermittently exposed to artificial sources at work. So the hazards associated with exposure to solar radiation provide a measure against which to judge the hazards of artificial sources such as sunbeds or ultraviolet lamps in the workplace.

Non-melanoma skin cancers are mainly of the kinds known as basal cell carcinomas and squamous cell carcinomas. They are fairly common in white people but rarely fatal. The overall incidence is difficult to assess: reported cases account for over 5% of registered malignancies in the UK and under 0.5% of cancer deaths, but rates are increasing every year.

These cancers occur most frequently on parts of the body exposed to the sun, such as the ears, face, head and hands, and become more common with increasing age. Epidemiological studies indicate that the risk of both cancers can be related to cumulative ultraviolet radiation exposure, although the evidence is stronger for squamous cell carcinomas. UVB has been recognised for some time as being carcinogenic in laboratory animals; there is increasing evidence that UVA, which penetrates more deeply into the skin, also contributes to the induction of cancer.

Malignant melanoma is the main cause of death from skin cancer, particularly in young people, although the incidence is less than that for non-melanoma types. The risk of developing malignant melanoma has increased markedly in white people: the annual incidence in the UK is about 10 new cases per 100 000 of the population, a doubling of the rate in less than two decades. The disease is relatively significant for young people: it constitutes 1 in 12 cancers and 1 in 25 cancer deaths for those aged 20 to 39 years.

Figures are higher for people with large numbers of naevi or moles and those with several unusual moles, for those with fair skin, red or blond hair, and for those with a tendency to freckle, to sunburn and not to tan. Both acute sunburn and regular exposure at work or at leisure probably contribute to the risk of malignant melanoma. It also seems that excessive exposure to the sun during the first 20 years of life increases the risk later on, although the precise nature of this relationship is uncertain.

As with all malignant disease, early diagnosis and treatment of malignant melanoma is important for patients. Since protection is better than cure, NRPB has made recommendations to minimise the effects of ultraviolet radiation on human health.

Measures to minimise danger from the sun
Prevent sunburn especially in childhood
Avoid the summer sun from 11 to 3 o'clock
Wear suitable protective clothes and a hat
Apply sunblocks or sunscreens

Long-term exposure to the sun causes photoageing of the skin, characterised by a leathery wrinkled appearance and loss of elasticity. Extensive biological studies have provided evidence that ultraviolet radiation has a rôle in causing these effects.

13
*Optical
radiation*

*Ultraviolet
radiation*

Some degree of exposure to ultraviolet radiation is beneficial in that it brings about the synthesis of vitamin D in the skin, which stimulates the absorption of calcium from the gut to bones. Although this may be important for some people on a restricted diet, for most people the harmful effects on the skin are far more significant.

Brief overexposure of the eyes to ultraviolet radiation can cause photokeratitis and photoconjunctivitis – inflammation of the cornea and conjunctiva, respectively. Repeated exposure is considered to be a major cause of non-malignant changes such as pterygium – an overgrowth of the conjunctiva on to the cornea.

Epidemiological data on the formation of cataracts in highly exposed people suggest that cumulative exposure to ultraviolet radiation is an important factor in the development of cataracts: the degree to which exposure is a significant risk factor for cataracts generally is however unclear.

There have been few appropriate studies with animals, but acute exposures to UVB at levels above the threshold for photokeratitis have induced opacities at the front of the lens.

NRPB monitors the levels of solar radiation throughout Great Britain. It has a network of six sites, one at every two degrees of latitude from the south of England to the north of Scotland. Continuous measurements are made of visible radiation, UVA, and erythemally weighted ultraviolet radiation. The accumulating data are useful for examining the effects of ultraviolet radiation on public health and the influence of climatic and other factors on exposures at ground level.

Other optical radiations

In this section, we shall refer to *visible radiation* and *infrared radiation* but dwell on lasers.

Human beings are adapted to the visible radiation from the sun. Eyes are normally protected from acute injury by bright light through involuntary responses such as blinking or averting one's gaze. These actions protect the retina from visible – and UVA – radiation that would otherwise be focused on it. Blue light is, however, the major hazard for the retina and is responsible for photochemical injury. As the sun sets and reddens, the rays become less hazardous.

13

Optical radiation

Other optical radiations

Lerwick

Kinloss

Glasgow

Leeds

Chilton

Camborne

UVR monitoring sites in Britain

Sunlight probably causes more optical injuries than artificial sources of optical radiation. However, some modern sources can have significant potential for injury, possibly within the reflex time for aversion. With some sources such as lasers, it is important to have precautions that do not rely upon the aversion response.

Research shows that the retina can degenerate when subjected to abnormally high levels of ambient illumination, particularly if the illumination is constant. It may well be that continual exposure to light plays a part in retinal ageing, a view confirmed by the similarities between changes in the retina from ageing and those caused by exposure to intense illumination.

Anterior parts of the eye, and specifically the lens, may be damaged by IRA radiation. Infrared radiation can also produce cataracts by thermal processes and burn the cornea. Experience indicates, however, that such injuries can be prevented by protective eyewear.

The main hazard to the skin from intense sources of visible and infrared radiations, such as lasers, is thermal burning. These devices deserve special mention.

Lasers emit optical radiation at one or a few discrete wavelengths throughout most of the optical spectrum from 100 nm to 1 mm. They are identified by the active medium – gas, liquid or solid – with solid lasers being divided into materials such as crystals and semiconductors. Lasers are widely used in commerce, industry, medicine, and in the home.

A laser differs from other sources of optical radiation in that the beam is usually intense and well collimated. The degree of harm that the beam causes is related to the irradiance, that is, the power per unit area. For other sources, this quantity decreases steeply with distance, but not necessarily with a laser source. A laser beam in the visible or IRA region falling on the surface of the eye will be focused nearly to a point; the result is that the irradiance at the surface will be increased by a factor of 100 000 or so at the retina.

The smallest value of irradiance likely to cause harm is 25 W m^{-2} in the visible region for an aversion response of 0.25 s; it corresponds to a power of 1 mW into a pupil of 7 mm diameter for the same period. In the visible region, with a helium-neon or ruby laser for example, the potential harm is a

13
Optical radiation

....

Other optical radiations

Effect of lasers on the human eye

100 watt bulb

Laser

Characteristics and applications of various types of laser			
ACTIVE MEDIUM	EXAMPLES	WAVELENGTHS (nm)	APPLICATIONS
Gas	Helium-neon	543.5, 632.8, 1152.6	Alignment, barcode scanning, printing, measurement
	Carbon dioxide	10 600	Cutting, welding, surgery
	Argon-ion	488, 514.5	Entertainment, surgery, printing, measurement
Liquid	Dye lasers	310–1200 dye dependent	Entertainment, medical diagnosis, measurement
Solid	Neodymium:YAG	1064, 532	Cutting, welding, entertainment, surgery
	Ruby	694.3	Holography, surgery
Semiconductor	Various	600–29000	Communications, pointers, compact disc players

thermal lesion of the retina. With a carbon dioxide laser, which emits in the infrared region, lesions tend to occur in the cornea.

International and national standards of safety for lasers exist: they include values of *maximum permissible exposure*, at various wavelengths, that are likely to cause harm to the eye. Values are also set for the skin itself where the harm can range from a mild erythema to severe burning of the skin and supporting tissues.

A classification scheme has been devised for laser products to indicate the degree of hazard for the user. It ranges from class 1 products with enclosed beams, as in printers or compact disc players, to class 4 products with open high-power beams, as in engineering or entertainment. For lasers, the watchword is precaution: damage can be done in the blink of an eye.

Appendix A
Glossary

Absorbed dose Quantity of energy imparted by *ionising radiation* to unit mass of matter such as tissue. Unit gray, symbol Gy. 1 Gy = 1 joule per kilogram.

Actinides A group of 15 *elements* with *atomic number* from that of actinium (89) to lawrencium (103) inclusive. All are radioactive. Group includes uranium, plutonium, americium, and curium.

Activity Attribute of an amount of a *radionuclide*. Describes the rate at which transformations occur in it. Unit becquerel, symbol Bq. 1 Bq = 1 transformation per second.

Advanced Gas Cooled Reactor A development of the *Magnox reactor*, using *enriched uranium* oxide fuel in stainless steel cladding.

AGR *Advanced gas cooled reactor*.

Alpha particle A particle consisting of two *protons* plus two *neutrons*. Emitted by a *radionuclide*.

Atom The smallest portion of an *element* that can combine chemically with other atoms.

Atomic bomb See *nuclear weapon*.

Atomic mass The mass of an *isotope* of an *element* expressed in atomic mass units, which are defined as one-twelfth of the mass of an *atom* of carbon-12.

Atomic number The number of *protons* in the *nucleus* of an *atom*. Symbol Z.

Becquerel See *activity*.

Beta particle An *electron* emitted by the *nucleus* of a *radionuclide*. The electric charge may be positive, in which case the beta particle is called a positron.

Brachytherapy Term applied to the use of radiation sources in or on the body for treating certain types of cancer.

Chromosomes Rod-shaped bodies found in the *nucleus of cells* in the body. They contain the *genes*, or hereditary constituents. Human beings possess 23 pairs.

Collective dose Frequently used for *collective effective dose*.

Collective effective dose The quantity obtained by multiplying the average *effective dose* by the number of people exposed to a given source of *ionising radiation*. Unit man sievert, symbol man Sv. Frequently abbreviated to collective dose.

Consumer products Personal and household goods such as timepieces, smoke alarms, and gas mantles that contain *radioactive* material for functional reasons.

Cosmic rays High energy *ionising radiations* from outer space. Complex composition at the surface of the earth.

Current density The electric current or flow of electric charge through a conducting medium, such as tissue, per unit cross-sectional area. Unit ampere per square metre, symbol $A\,m^{-2}$.

Decay The process of spontaneous transformation of a *radionuclide*. The decrease in the activity of a *radioactive* substance.

Decay product A *nuclide* or *radionuclide* produced by *decay*. It may be formed directly from a radionuclide or as a result of a series of successive decays through several radionuclides.

**Appendix A
Glossary**

Decommissioning The process of closing down a *nuclear reactor*, removing the spent fuel, dismantling some of the other components, and preparing them for *disposal*. Term may also be applied to other major nuclear facilities.

Diagnostic radiology Term usually applied to the use of *X-rays* in medicine for identifying disease or injury in patients.

Disposal In relation to *radioactive waste*, dispersal or emplacement in any medium without the intention of retrieval.

DNA Deoxyribonucleic acid. The compound that controls the structure and function of cells and is the material of inheritance.

Dose General term for quantity of *ionising radiation*. See *absorbed dose, equivalent dose, effective dose* and *collective effective dose*. Frequently used for effective dose.

Effective dose The quantity obtained by multiplying the *equivalent dose* to various tissues and organs by a weighting factor appropriate to each and summing the products. Unit sievert, symbol Sv. Tissue weighting factors are tabulated in Chapter 2. Frequently abbreviated to dose.

Electrical interaction A force of repulsion acting between electric charges of like sign and a force of attraction acting between electric charges of unlike sign.

Electric field strength A measure of the intensity of an electric field. Unit volt per metre, symbol $V\,m^{-1}$.

Electromagnetic field The region in which *electromagnetic radiation* from a source exerts an influence on another object with or without there being contact between them.

Electromagnetic radiation *Radiation* that can be considered as a wave of electric and magnetic energy travelling through a vacuum or a material. Examples are *gamma rays, X-rays, ultraviolet radiation, light, infrared radiation* and *radiofrequency radiation*.

Electromagnetic spectrum All *electromagnetic radiations* displayed as a continuum in order of increasing *frequency* or decreasing *wavelength*.

Electromagnetic wave See *electromagnetic radiation*.

Electron An elementary particle with low mass, $1/1836$ that of a proton, and unit negative electric charge. Positively charged electrons, called positrons, also exist. See also *beta particle*.

Electron volt Unit of energy employed in radiation physics. Equal to the energy gained by an electron in passing through a potential difference of 1 volt. Symbol eV. $1\,eV = 1.6 \times 10^{-19}$ joule approximately.

Element A substance with atoms all of the same *atomic number*.

Emergency reference level One of a dual set of *doses* likely to be averted by the introduction of countermeasures to protect the public from *ionising radiation* after a nuclear or other serious accident.

EMF *Electromagnetic field*. Not to be confused with the initials for electromotive force.

Enriched uranium Uranium in which the content of the *isotope* uranium-235 has been increased above its natural value of 0.7% by weight.

Equivalent dose The quantity obtained by multiplying the *absorbed dose* by a factor to allow for the different effectiveness of the various *ionising radiations* in causing harm to tissue. Unit sievert, symbol Sv. Radiation weighting factors are given in Chapter 2.

ERL See *emergency reference level* of dose.

Erythema Reddening of the skin caused by dilation of blood vessels.

Excitation A process by which *radiation* imparts energy to an *atom* or *molecule* without causing *ionisation*. Dissipated as heat in tissue.

Fallout The transfer of *radionuclides* produced by *nuclear weapons* from the atmosphere to earth; the material transferred.

Fast neutrons Conventionally, neutrons with energies in excess of 0.1 MeV. Corresponding velocity of about $4 \times 10^{6}\,m\,s^{-1}$.

Fast reactors See *nuclear reactor*.

Fission Nuclear fission. A process in which a *nucleus* splits into two or more nuclei and energy is released. Frequently refers to the splitting of a nucleus of uranium-235 into two approximately equal parts by a *thermal neutron* with emission of other neutrons.

Fission products *Nuclides* or *radionuclides* produced as a result of *fission*.

Free radical A grouping of *atoms* that normally exists in combination with other atoms but can sometimes exist independently. Generally very reactive in a chemical sense.

Frequency The number of complete cycles of an *electromagnetic wave* in a second. Unit hertz, symbol Hz. 1 Hz = 1 cycle per second.

Fusion Thermonuclear fusion. A process in which two or more light *nuclei* are formed into a heavier nucleus and energy is released.

Gamma ray A discrete quantity of electromagnetic energy without mass or charge. Emitted by a *radionuclide*. Cf *X-ray*.

Geiger-Müller tube A glass or metal envelope containing a gas at low pressure and two electrodes. *Ionising radiation* causes discharges, which are registered as electric pulses in a counter. The number of pulses is related to *dose*.

Genes The biological units of heredity. They are arranged along the length of *chromosomes*.

Gray See *absorbed dose*.

Half-life The time taken for the *activity* of a *radionuclide* to lose half its value by *decay*. Symbol $t^1/_2$.

Infrared radiation *Electromagnetic radiation* capable of producing the sensation of heat and found between *light* and *radiofrequency radiations* in the *electromagnetic spectrum*. Has subregions IRA, IRB and IRC.

Ion Electrically charged *atom* or grouping of atoms.

Ionisation The process by which a neutral *atom* or *molecule* acquires or loses an electric charge. The production of *ions*.

Ionising radiation *Radiation* that produces *ionisation* in matter. Examples are *alpha particles, gamma rays, X-rays* and *neutrons*. When these radiations pass through the tissues of the body, they have sufficient energy to damage *DNA*.

Irradiance The power per unit area of *optical radiation*. Unit watt per square metre, symbol $W\,m^{-2}$.

Isotope *Nuclides* with the same number of *protons* but different numbers of *neutrons*. Not a synonym for nuclide.

Laser Device which amplifies *light* and usually produces an extremely narrow intense beam of a single *wavelength*.

Light *Electromagnetic radiation* capable of producing the sensation of vision and found between *ultraviolet* and *infrared radiations* in the *electromagnetic spectrum*.

Magnetic flux density A measure of the magnetic effect induced in a medium by an external field. Unit tesla, symbol T.

Magnox reactor A *thermal reactor* named after the magnesium alloy in which the uranium metal fuel is contained. The *moderator* is graphite and the coolant is carbon dioxide gas.

Man sievert See *collective effective dose*.

Mass number The number of *protons* plus *neutrons* in the *nucleus* of an *atom*. Symbol *A*.

Maximum permissible exposure The *irradiance* likely to cause detectable damage to the human eye or skin from exposure to *optical radiation*. Unit watt per square metre, symbol $W\,m^{-2}$.

Moderator A material used in *nuclear reactors* to reduce the energy and speed of the *neutrons* produced as a result of *fission*.

Molecule The smallest portion of a substance that can exist by itself and retain the properties of the substance.

Mutation A chemical change in the *DNA* in the *nucleus of a cell*. Mutations in sperm or egg cells or their precursors may lead to inherited effects in children. Mutations in body cells may lead to effects in the individual.

Neutron An elementary particle with unit *atomic mass* approximately and no electric charge.

Non-ionising radiation *Radiation* that does not produce *ionisation* in matter. Examples are *ultraviolet radiation, light, infrared radiation* and *radiofrequency radiation*. When these radiations pass through the tissues of the body they do not have sufficient energy to damage *DNA* directly.

Nuclear fuel cycle The stages in which the fuel for *nuclear reactors* is first prepared, then used, and later reprocessed for possible use again. *Waste management* is also considered part of the cycle.

Nuclear medicine Term usually applied to the use of *radionuclides* for diagnosing or treating disease in patients.

Nuclear power Power obtained from the operation of a *nuclear reactor*. Refers in the text to electric power.

Nuclear power industry The industry associated with the production of *nuclear power*. In the United Kingdom, the preparation of fuel for *nuclear reactors*, the operation of reactors, the subsequent reprocessing of the fuel, and the *disposal of radioactive wastes*.

Nuclear reactor A device in which nuclear *fission* can be sustained in a self-supporting chain reaction involving *neutrons*. In thermal reactors, fission is brought about by *thermal neutrons*.

Nuclear weapon Explosive device deriving its power from *fission* or *fusion* of *nuclei* or from both.

Nucleus The core of an *atom*, occupying little of the volume, containing most of the mass, and bearing positive electric charge.

Nucleus of a cell The controlling centre of the basic unit of tissue. Contains the important material *DNA*.

Nuclide A species of *atom* characterised by the number of *protons* and *neutrons* and, in some cases, by the energy state of the *nucleus*.

Optical radiation *Electromagnetic radiation* comprising *ultraviolet, visible* and *infrared radiations*.

Order of magnitude Quantity given to the nearest power of ten. A factor of ten or so.

Ozone A form of oxygen gas which occurs naturally in very small quantities in air. Most of the ozone is in the stratosphere where it forms the ozone layer.

Photographic film Film with emulsion sensitive to *ionising radiation*. The degree of blackening is related to dose.

Photon A quantum of *electromagnetic radiation*.

Positron See *beta particle*.

Power density The power per unit cross sectional area in an *electromagnetic field*. Unit watt per square metre, symbol Wm^{-2}.

Pressurised water reactor A *thermal reactor* using water as both a *moderator* and coolant. Uses *enriched uranium* oxide fuel.

Probability The mathematical chance that a given event will occur.

Proton An elementary particle with unit *atomic mass* approximately and unit positive electric charge.

PWR *Pressurised water reactor*.

Radiation The process of emitting energy as waves or particles. The energy thus radiated. Frequently used for *ionising radiation* in the text except when it is necessary to avoid confusion with *non-ionising radiation*.

Radioactive Possessing the property of *radioactivity*.

Radioactive waste Useless material containing *radionuclides*. Frequently categorised in the *nuclear power industry* according to *activity* and other criteria given in Chapter 10, as low level, intermediate level, and high level waste.

Radioactivity The property of *radionuclides* of spontaneously emitting *ionising radiation*.

Radiobiology The study of the effects of *ionising radiation* on living things.

Radiofrequency radiation *Electromagnetic radiation* used for telecommunications and found in the *electromagnetic spectrum* at longer *wavelengths* than *infrared radiation*.

RF See *radiofrequency radiation*.

Radiological protection The science and practice of limiting the harm to human beings from *radiation*.

Radionuclide An unstable *nuclide* that emits *ionising radiation*.

Radiotherapy Term applied to the use of radiation beams for treating disease, usually cancers, in patients.

Reference accident One of a range of accidents at a *nuclear reactor* or other nuclear installation that can reasonably be foreseen in safety analysis as giving rise to the most significant release of *radionuclides* from the site.

Risk The *probability* of injury, harm or damage.

Risk factor The *probability* of cancer and leukaemia or hereditary damage per unit *equivalent dose*. Usually refers to fatal malignant diseases and serious hereditary damage. Unit Sv^{-1}.

Scintillation counter A device containing material that emits light flashes when exposed to *ionising radiation*. The flashes are converted to electric pulses and counted. The number of pulses is related to dose.

Sievert See *effective dose*.

Silicon diode A device made of a silicon compound in which current flows when exposed to *ionising radiation*. The current is converted to electrical pulses and counted. The number of pulses is related to dose.

Specific energy absorption rate The rate at which energy is absorbed by unit mass of tissue in an *electromagnetic field*. Unit watt per kilogram, symbol $W \, kg^{-1}$.

SAR See *specific energy absorption rate*.

Thermal neutrons *Neutrons* that have been slowed to the degree that they have the same average thermal energy as the *atoms* or *molecules* through which they are passing. The average energy of neutrons at ordinary temperatures is about $0.025 \, eV$, corresponding to an average velocity of $2.2 \times 10^3 \, m \, s^{-1}$.

Thermal reactor See *nuclear reactor*.

Thermoluminescent material Material which, having been irradiated, releases light in proportion to the *ionising radiation* absorbed when it is subsequently heated.

Ultraviolet radiation *Electromagnetic radiation* found between *X-rays* and *light* in the *electromagnetic spectrum*. Has subregions UVA, UVB, UVC.

UVR See *ultraviolet radiation*.

Visible radiation See *light*.

Waste management The control of *radioactive waste* from creation to *disposal*.

Wavelength The distance between successive crests of an *electromagnetic wave* passing through a given material. Unit metre, symbol m.

X-ray A discrete quantity of electromagnetic energy without mass or charge. Emitted by an X-ray machine. Cf *gamma ray*.

Appendix B
Symbols and units

Scientific notation

It is often more convenient to express the numbers encountered in radiological protection in scientific rather than decimal notation because of their magnitude. This involves the use of significant figures within desired limits and multiplication by the appropriate power of ten. Examples follow.

Converting decimal to scientific notation

DECIMAL	SCIENTIFIC
1 230 000	1.23×10^6
100 000	10^5
3 531	$3.53 \times 10^{3*}$
15.6	1.56×10^1
0.239	$2.4 \times 10^{-1}†$
0.001	10^{-3}
0.000 087	8.7×10^{-5}

*To three significant figures.
†To two significant figures.

Prefixes

Some powers of ten have special names and symbols. These may be prefixed to units of measurement: thus *kilogram*, symbol kg, for 10^3 gram; *millimetre*, symbol mm, for 10^{-3} metre. A table of prefixes follows.

Prefixes

MULTIPLIER	PREFIX	SYMBOL	MULTIPLIER	PREFIX	SYMBOL
10^1	deca	da	10^{-1}	deci	d
10^2	hecto	h	10^{-2}	centi	c
10^3	kilo	k	10^{-3}	milli	m
10^6	mega	M	10^{-6}	micro	μ
10^9	giga	G	10^{-9}	nano	n
10^{12}	tera	T	10^{-12}	pico	p
10^{15}	peta	P	10^{-15}	femto	f
10^{18}	exa	E	10^{-18}	atto	a
10^{21}	zetta	Z	10^{-21}	zepto	z
10^{24}	yotta	Y	10^{-24}	yocto	y

Symbols

Symbols are used extensively in radiological protection. The elements are usually represented by symbols, for example, C for carbon, Ba for barium, and Pb for lead. It is usual to indicate the mass number and atomic number of a particular nuclide by a superscript and subscript thus:

carbon-14 by $^{14}_{6}C$,
barium-140 by $^{140}_{56}Ba$,
lead-210 by $^{210}_{82}Pb$.

The atomic number is frequently omitted.

A table of common symbols follows. When the symbol for a unit is shown with a superscript of -1 on its right, it signifies that the quantity is being used in a fractional context or to represent rate. Thus $Sv\,h^{-1}$ means sievert *per* hour.

Table of common symbols in radiological protection			
SYMBOL	TERM	SYMBOL	TERM
α	alpha particle	A	mass number
β	beta particle	eV	electron volt
γ	gamma ray	Bq	becquerel
e	electron	Gy	gray
p	protron	Sv	sievert
n	neutron	man Sv	man sievert
Z	atomic number	$t\,{}^{1}/_{2}$	half-life

Quantities and units for ionising radiation

Some time ago, the units for the main ionising radiation quantities were changed to those used in this text. Readers may come across old units: this table shows how to convert them to the new units.

Relationship between old and new ionising radiation units					
QUANTITY	OLD UNIT	SYMBOL	NEW UNIT	SYMBOL	RELATIONSHIP
Activity	curie	Ci	becquerel	Bq	$1\,Ci = 3.7 \times 10^{10}\,Bq$
Absorbed dose	rad	rad	gray	Gy	$1\,rad = 0.01\,Gy$
Equivalent dose*	rem	rem	sievert	Sv	$1\,rem = 0.01\,Sv$

*Was dose equivalent.

Quantities and units for non-ionising radiation

Appendix B
Symbols
and units

Radiometric quantities

Quantity	Unit
Radiant energy	joule (J)
Radiant flux	watt (W)
Irradiance	$W\,m^{-2}$
Radiant intensity	$W\,sr^{-1}$*
Radiance	$W\,sr^{-1}\,m^{-2}$
Radiant exposure	$J\,m^{-2}$
Spectral irradiance	$W\,m^{-2}\,nm^{-1}$†
Spectral radiance	$W\,sr^{-1}\,m^{-2}\,nm^{-1}$

*The steradian (sr) is the unit of solid angle.
† Wavelength in nanometres (10^{-9} m).

Photometric quantities

Quantity	Unit
Luminous energy	lumen second
Luminous flux	lumen (lm)
Illuminance	lux* (lx)
Luminous intensity	$lm\,sr^{-1}$
Luminance	$cd\,m^{-2}$†

*lux = lumen per square metre.
† candela (cd).

Characterisation of exposure fields

Quantity	Unit
Frequency	hertz (Hz)
Wavelength	metre (m)
Electric field strength	volt per metre ($V\,m^{-1}$)
Magnetic field strength*	ampere per metre ($A\,m^{-1}$)
Magnetic flux density*	tesla (T)
Power density	watt per square metre ($W\,m^{-2}$)

*A magnetic field strength of 1 $A\,m^{-1}$ is equivalent to a magnetic flux density of $4\pi\,10^{-7}$ T in non-magnetic media.

Dosimetric quantities

Quantity	Unit
Current density	ampere per square metre ($A\,m^{-2}$)
Specific energy absorption rate (SAR)	watt per kilogram ($W\,kg^{-1}$)

Appendix C
NRPB publications

Apart from this book, NRPB publishes a wide range of material on radiological protection for a professional and public readership.

Documents of the NRPB, the prime publications, contain formal advice and findings on important issues with appropriate supplementary material. Some are as substantial as textbooks with definitive treatment of radiological topics.

NRPB publishes the results of research in scientific journals. Some scientific material may also appear in the *NRPB Report* series and technical matter in the *NRPB Memorandum* series. Voluminous scientific data are made available in *NRPB Software*; personal computer codes are also produced. News and reviews, articles and reports appear in the *Radiological Protection Bulletin* which is widely read by professionals.

At the popular end of the range of NRPB publications are the *At-a-Glance* leaflets on radiation topics for members of the public generally and science pupils particularly; they unfold to poster size. Similar publications are prepared for industrial and other employees in the *Radiation-at-Work* series. A video on radon in the home has also been produced.

NRPB has a site on the Internet at http://www.nrpb.org.uk, which includes details of current publications.